Exploring
EARTH AND SPACE SCIENCE

11

Index

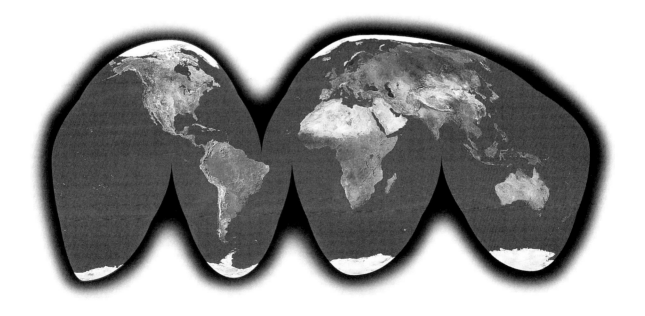

Marshall Cavendish
New York • London • Toronto • Sydney

Marshall Cavendish Corporation
99 White Plains Road
Tarrytown, New York 10591-9001

Website: www.marshallcavendish.com

© 2002 Marshall Cavendish Corporation

Created by **Brown Partworks Limited**

Library of Congress Cataloging-in-Publication Data

Exploring earth and space science.
    p. cm.
    Includes bibliographical references and indexes.
    Contents: 1. Acid and base-Calcium -- 2. Calendar-Continental shelf -- 3. Copper-El
Niño and La Niña -- 4. Energy-Gondwana -- 5. Grassland-Laser -- 6. Light-Meteor -- 7.
Meteorology-Ordovician period -- 8. Ore-Prospecting -- 9. Protein-Star -- 10.
Stratosphere-X ray -- 11. Index.
    ISBN 0-7614-7219-3 (set) -- ISBN 0-7614-7220-7 (v. 1) -- ISBN 0-7614-7221-5 (v. 2)
-- ISBN 0-7614-7222-3 (v. 3) -- ISBN 0-7614-7223-1 (v. 4) -- ISBN 0-7614-7224-X (v.
5) -- ISBN 0-7614-7225-8 (v. 6) -- ISBN 0-7614-7226-6 (v. 7) -- ISBN 0-7614-7227-4
(v. 8) -- ISBN 0-7614-7228-2 (v. 9) -- ISBN 0-7614-7229-0 (v. 10) -- ISBN
0-7614-7230-4 (v. 11)
    1. Earth sciences--Encyclopedias. 2. Space sciences--Encyclopedias. 3.
Astronomy--Encyclopedias

QE5 .E96 2002

550'.3--dc21
                  00-065801
                  CIP
                  AC

ISBN 0-7614-7219-3 (set)

ISBN 0-7614-7230-4 (vol. 11)

Printed in Hong Kong

06 05 04 03 02 01 00 5 4 3 2 1

PHOTOGRAPHIC CREDITS

Corbis: World Panoramas *824-25, 826-27, 828-29, 830-31*
Science Photo Library: Eye of Science *804*

Front cover: Computer image of the surface of Earth without water (NOAA/NGDC)

Title page: Projection of Earth's land and oceans (Science Photo Library, Worldsat
        International and J. Knighton)

Back cover: How position of Earth changes as it orbits the Sun every year (Marshall Cavendish)

Exploring

EARTH AND SPACE SCIENCE

11

Index

Contents	803	GLOSSARY	824
Weights and Measures	804	SUBJECT INDEXES	
The Story of Space	806	Chemistry	832
The Atomic World	808	Earth	837
Inside Earth	810	Environment	843
Geologic Timescale	812	Physics	844
Science Time Line	814	Space Science	848
Periodic Table	816	Technology	851
Places to Go	818	People	853
Things to Do	821	Places	856
		GENERAL INDEX	858

Marshall Cavendish
New York • London • Toronto • Sydney

Weights and Measures

IMPERIAL TO METRIC

WEIGHT
Multiply:
__ ounces by 28.35 to get __ grams (g)
__ pounds by 0.454 to get __ kilograms (kg)
__ tons by .907 to get __ tonnes

VOLUME
Multiply:
__ quarts by 0.9461 to get __ liters (l)

TEMPERATURE
First subtract 32 from the Fahrenheit (°F) number, then multiply by 0.5556 to get the Celsius (°C; centigrade) number.

LENGTH
Multiply:
__ inches by 25.4 to get __ millimeters (mm)
__ inches by 2.54 to get __ centimeters (cm)
__ feet by 0.305 to get __ meters (m)
__ miles by 1.609 to get __ kilometers (km)

AREA
Multiply:
__ sq feet by 0.093 to get __sq meters (sq m)
__ acres by 0.405 to get __ hectares (ha)

Imagining a million

The planets, stars, and the spaces between them are so huge that it requires a leap of the imagination to understand the distances involved. Sometimes it can help to break down a large distance, such as a million miles, into more familiar chunks. Imagine you travel 25 miles on the day you are born—and every day after that. When you are 109 years old, you will have traveled 1,000,000 miles.

Imagining one-millionth

The most powerful electron microscopes can magnify an object one million times. An object magnified in this way is one-millionth the size of the image. Imagine, just one of those miles you

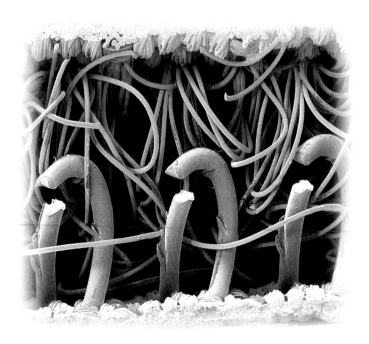

These Velcro hooks and loops are a tiny fraction of the size they appear in this electron micrograph.

METRIC TO IMPERIAL

WEIGHT
Multiply:
___ grams (g) by 0.035 to get ___ ounces
___ kilograms (kg) by 2.2 to get ___ pounds
___ tonnes by 1.102 to get ___ tons

VOLUME
Multiply:
___ liters (l) by 1.057 to get ___ quarts

TEMPERATURE
First multiply the Celsius (°C; centigrade) number by 1.80, then add 32 to get the Fahrenheit (°F) number.

LENGTH
Multiply:
___ millimeters (mm) by 0.039 to get ___ inches
___ centimeters (cm) by 0.39 to get ___ inches
___ meters (m) by 3.28 to get ___ feet
___ kilometers (km) by 0.621 to get ___ miles

AREA
Multiply:
___ sq meters (sq m) by 10.764 to get ___ sq feet
___ hectares (ha) by 2.47 to get ___ acres

travel—1 mile out of 1,000,000—is one-millionth ($\frac{1}{1,000,000}$) of the total distance.

How far is a light-year?
Large distances are often expressed in astronomical units (AU) or light-years. An AU is the average distance between Earth and the Sun. One AU = 93,000,000 miles = 149,600,000 km.

It takes about eight minutes for the light from the Sun to travel to Earth. One light-year is the distance a light beam would travel through a vacuum in one year. One light-year = 5,878,000,000,000 miles = 9,460,500,000,000 km = 63,240 AU.

Weight
1 gram (1 g) = 1 paper clip
1 kilogram (1 kg) = 1,000 g
= 8 bananas

Temperature
Water boils at 212°F or 100°C
Water freezes at 32°F or 0°C
Body temperature is 98.6°F or 37°C

Area
1 acre = a football field without the end zones
1 square mile = 640 acres
Washington, D.C., covers 67 square miles

Length
1 millimeter (1 mm) = thickness of a penny
1 centimeter (1 cm) = 10 mm
1 meter (1 m) = 100 cm = 1,000 mm

Decimals and Fractions
Decimals are another way of showing fractions.
One-half = ½ = 0.5; one-third = ⅓ = 0.333;
one-quarter = ¼ = 0.25; and one-tenth = ⅒ = 0.1

The Story of Space

People have stargazed for thousands of years. Before the 20th century, however, few astronomers imagined that space extended beyond Earth's galaxy, the Milky Way. The discovery of distant galaxies in the 1920s triggered findings that, when pieced together, make up a history of the Universe.

The Big Bang

The birth of the Universe is thought to have happened 12 billion years ago. In less than a second, all the matter in the Universe exploded out from a point far tinier than an atom. This explosion is called the Big Bang. Echoes of this outpouring of energy can still be detected.

After millions of years, matter began to cluster to form stars and galaxies. Huge modern telescopes allow astronomers to see back into these early moments of the Universe. This is because they can detect distant objects whose light has taken billions of years to reach Earth.

The young Solar System

The Sun formed from a cloud of gas and dust around 4.6 billion years ago. The planets in the Solar System formed from clusters of material left behind, sweeping up the matter orbiting the young Sun as their mass and gravity increased. Matter that was not captured by the planets' gravity collided and clumped together over millions of years, forming asteroids and comets.

On the outer edge of the Solar System, bodies such as Pluto and Neptune's moon Triton formed from ices that had not been heated by the Sun. Beyond these cold worlds, the Solar System is surrounded by a shell of other frozen objects, called the Oort cloud.

Understanding space

The Universe is still expanding from its initial explosive creation. It may be shaped like a bubble, pulled around by its huge mass. Scientists think the Universe will expand in this way forever but will eventually run out of energy, and then there will be no more heat or light.

The formation of the Sun

The Sun began to form when a cloud of dust and gas was hit by the shock wave from an exploding star. The material in the cloud clumped together and began to rotate.

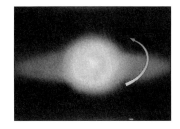

The rotating cloud began to bulge at the center. As the bulge—the young Sun—grew, its gravity became stronger. It pulled in more mass and rotated faster.

The pressure and temperature in the Sun's core led to nuclear fusion of hydrogen into helium. The Sun began to generate energy and release it into space.

Solar energy

The Sun, like all stars in space, generates energy from nuclear reactions in its core. Stars do not shine forever. When the nuclear fuel in the core runs out, the outer layers will no longer be puffed out by the pressure of this energy rushing out. A star the size of the Sun will collapse into a tiny, dead star called a white dwarf.

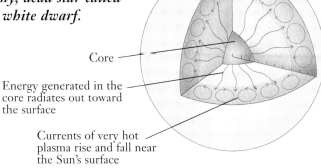

Core

Energy generated in the core radiates out toward the surface

Currents of very hot plasma rise and fall near the Sun's surface

The planets

Each planet formed at a different distance from the Sun. Those that formed in hotter regions, close to the Sun, are made up of different materials from the outer planets. Mercury, Venus, Earth, and Mars are the inner planets. They formed from materials that are solid at high temperatures, such as metals and rocks. Jupiter and the planets beyond contain more ice.

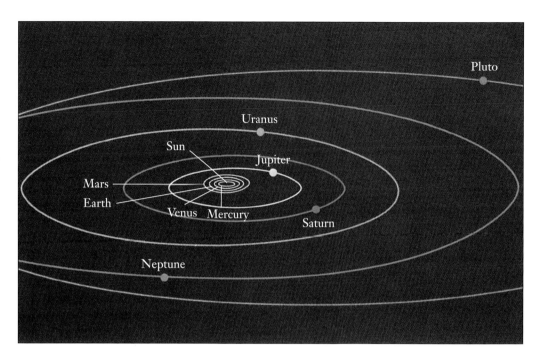

Exploring space

In the 1960s, the United States and the Soviet Union raced one another to put a person into space. Russian Yuri Gagarin became the first person to travel in space in 1961. With the Apollo mission, the United States then put the first men on Earth's Moon. The Apollo spacecraft consisted of three modules, including the lunar module that landed on the Moon.

Today, a number of nations are cooperating to set up a permanent orbiting laboratory in space—the International Space Station.

Space and time

German-born U.S. scientist Albert Einstein has shaped our understanding of the nature of space. Massive bodies, such as planets and stars, distort space and time around them. Even light does not escape the effects of their gravity.

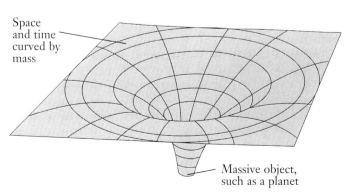

Space and time curved by mass

Massive object, such as a planet

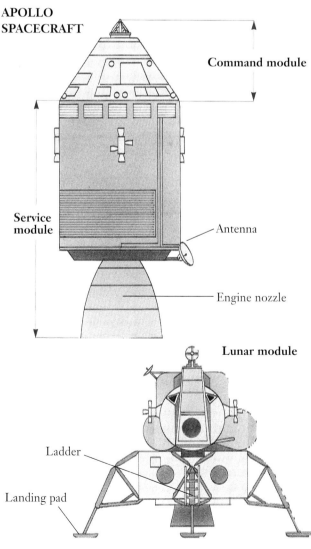

APOLLO SPACECRAFT

Command module

Service module

Antenna

Engine nozzle

Lunar module

Ladder

Landing pad

The Atomic World

Atoms formed from the remains of the Big Bang. The particles scattered by this explosion cooled and were transformed into the subatomic particles that make up all matter today. These grouped to form nuclei (atom centers) surrounded by swarms of electrons. Some 300,000 years after the explosion, the nuclei and electrons grouped to form atoms.

Discovering the atom

The idea that all matter is made up of tiny building blocks called atoms was first proposed by Greek scientist Democritus in the 4th century B.C.E. His theory, however, was overshadowed by fellow Greek Aristotle's theory that matter is made from five elements: air, earth, water, fire, and ether. Not until the 18th and 19th centuries did scientists prove that Democritus was right.

Inside the atom

While Democritus believed atoms to be the smallest particles in the Universe, 19th-century scientists found that atoms consist of three types of particles. These subatomic particles are protons (positive), neutrons (no charge), and electrons (negative). Protons and neutrons make up nearly all the mass of an atom, clustered in a nucleus at the center. Negatively charged electrons, only $\frac{1}{2,000}$ the mass of a proton, orbit the nucleus in clouds at different distances.

Subatomic forces

The forces that hold atoms together depend on tiny particles that are exchanged back and forth between protons, neutrons, and electrons. Splitting the nucleus of an atom, called nuclear fission, releases huge amounts of energy, which has been used in power plants and to make bombs. The behavior of subatomic particles is studied in particle accelerators, which fire beams of particles at one another. The particles split when they collide. There are, however, particles that are thought to be truly indivisible. These include electrons and particles called quarks, which make up protons and neutrons.

States of matter

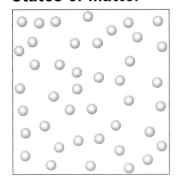

Gas

Atoms can exist singly in some gases but in most they group together as molecules. Gas molecules are separate and are moving constantly.

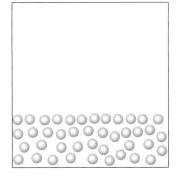

Liquid

In a liquid, the atoms or molecules attract each other and remain close together. They can slide around each other, making the liquid flow.

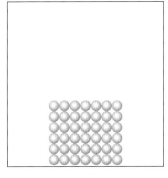

Solid

In most solids, the atoms attract each other strongly and form regular patterns. Force is required to break the bonds and split a solid.

Protons and neutrons

The protons and neutrons in an atom's nucleus are made up of smaller particles called quarks, which exchange particles called gluons. This exchange exerts a force that prevents the protons and neutrons from flying apart.

Neutrons are particles with no charge

Positively charged protons

Discovering the nucleus

British physicist Ernest Rutherford discovered the nucleus of the atom by firing tiny alpha particles at a sheet of gold foil. Most of the particles passed through, showing that the atoms in the gold are mostly empty space. However, some of these positively charged particles bounced back as if they had encountered a positively charged mass. These were the nuclei of the gold atoms.

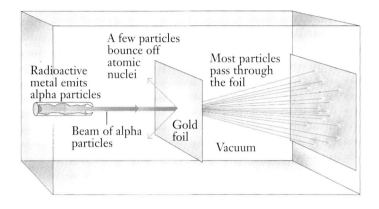

Radioactive metal emits alpha particles

A few particles bounce off atomic nuclei

Most particles pass through the foil

Beam of alpha particles

Gold foil

Vacuum

Nuclear fission

Fission begins when a neutron collides with the nucleus of an atom, for example, uranium 235. This atom nucleus splits into two smaller nuclei and more lone neutrons, releasing huge amounts of energy, called nuclear radiation.

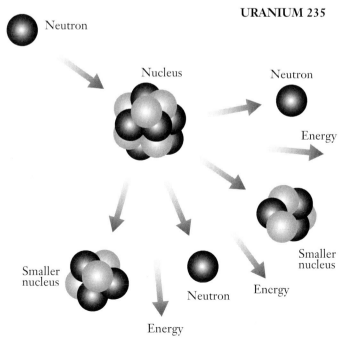

URANIUM 235

Neutron

Nucleus

Neutron

Energy

Energy

Smaller nucleus

Smaller nucleus

Neutron

Energy

Energy

Sharing electrons

Some molecules form when atoms share electrons. Three hydrogen atoms bond in this way with one nitrogen atom to form a pyramid-shaped molecule of ammonia—a pungent, colorless gas.

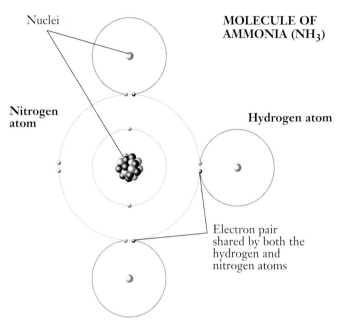

Nuclei

MOLECULE OF AMMONIA (NH₃)

Nitrogen atom

Hydrogen atom

Electron pair shared by both the hydrogen and nitrogen atoms

Polar molecules

Atoms have a positively charged nucleus at their center, surrounded by negatively charged electrons. Some atoms attract electrons more strongly than others. When a molecule contains two types of atoms, electrons from one are often pulled toward the other, making a polar molecule.

Nonpolar hydrogen (H_2) molecule

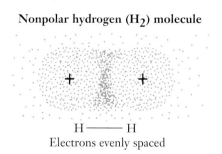

H ——— H
Electrons evenly spaced

Polar hydrogen chloride (HCl) molecule

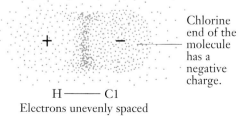

Chlorine end of the molecule has a negative charge.

H ——— Cl
Electrons unevenly spaced

Inside Earth

Earth is the third planet in the Solar System and it is thought to be the only one that supports life. It was formed more than 4.6 billion years ago along with the other eight planets, their moons, and countless smaller objects that make up the Solar System. Earth orbits at 93 million miles (150 million km) from the Sun and has a large satellite of its own, called the Moon.

Rocky world

Earth's atmosphere is mostly oxygen and nitrogen. Two-thirds of the Earth is covered by water. Like the other terrestrial planets of the inner Solar System (Mercury, Venus, and Mars), Earth is a rocky planet, but it is not solid rock from surface to center. Only the thin crust at the surface, which makes up the continents and the seabed, is rock hard. Underneath the crust, in the mantle, the rock becomes a hot liquid that is heated by a solid iron core at Earth's center.

Earth's crust is made up of sections of rock called plates, which float on top of the liquid mantle. Currents of molten rock (magma) in the mantle may push up and draw down the edges of these plates, causing ridges of volcanoes or deep trenches on Earth's surface.

New from old

When the molten rock pushes out toward the surface, it cools into a solid and becomes a new part of the crust. All rocks on Earth's surface were originally formed like this. However, some rocks are changed by the heat and pressure caused when mountains are squeezed up out of the ground. Others form from tiny grains that have been worn away from other rocks before being compressed into layers of new types of rock. Earth's crust is constantly being drawn back into the mantle, where it becomes magma again ready to form new rock, creating a cycle.

Scientists can work out how old a rock is by studying the fossils in it. Fossils are the remains of living organisms that have been turned to stone. Scientists have been able to piece together the history of Earth by studying fossils.

Earth's internal structure

This is a cross section of Earth. It shows the layers of crust, mantle, and core. Earth's crust is a mixture of thin ocean crust and thicker continental (land) crust. Below this is the mantle, which reaches down about 1,800 miles (2,900 km). The hot core is in the very center.

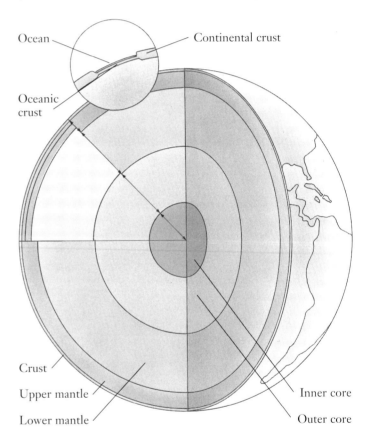

Ocean
Continental crust
Oceanic crust
Crust
Upper mantle
Lower mantle
Inner core
Outer core

Plate boundaries

The plates that make up the crust carry the continents and oceans. Where two plates meet, earthquakes, volcanoes, mountains, and trenches can form as magma is pushed up or plates are dragged down.

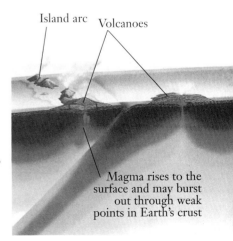

Island arc   Volcanoes

Magma rises to the surface and may burst out through weak points in Earth's crust

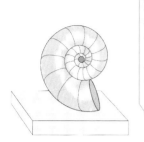

A dead sea creature sinks to the seabed.

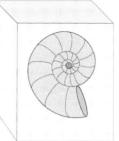

The animal's remains are buried in sand and mud.

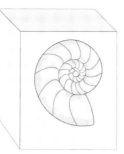

The soft parts and shell eventually dissolve, leaving a hollow.

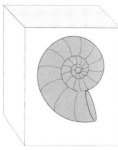

The hollow fills up with sediment that eventually turns to stone.

Fossilization

Geologists (scientists who study rocks) use fossils to figure out when and where a rock was formed. For example, fossils of fish have been found on top of mountains. This shows that the rocks in that mountain must have formed underwater.

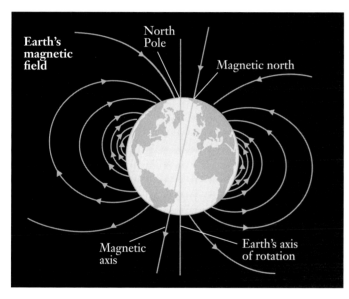

Magnetic fields

Earth has a magnetic field around it with north and south magnetic poles, just like that of a bar magnet. These poles are close to the geographic poles.

Earth's atmosphere

Earth's atmosphere has four main layers. These are the troposphere, stratosphere, mesosphere, and thermosphere. Earth's weather occurs in the troposphere. Strong winds called jet streams blow in the stratosphere. The mesosphere and themosphere contain only a fraction of Earth's air.

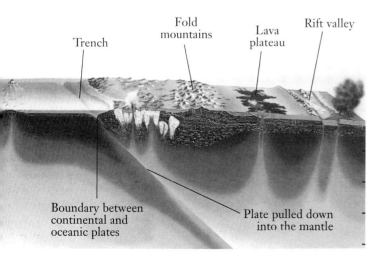

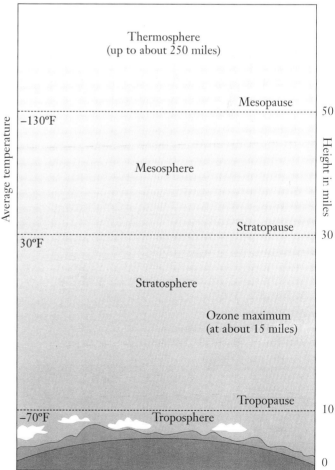

Geologic Timescale

The geologic timescale is a way of dividing Earth's history into sections. The divisions are often based on large-scale events that have left their mark on the environment and life of the time. Changes in the order of rock strata (STRAH-tuh; layers) and in the fossils they contain are evidence of these events. Geologists have used this evidence to construct Earth's history back to approximately 3.9 billion years ago—the age of the earliest rocks. The formative stage that pre-dates these rocks is named the Pre-Archean and dates back to Earth's formation 4.6 billion years ago. The biggest divisions in the geologic timescale are eons, which are groups of eras. Eras are groups of periods, which are themselves groups of epochs.

Era				Paleozoic				
Period		Cambrian	Ordovician	Silurian	Devonian	Carboniferous		Permian
						Mississippian	Pennsylvanian	
	Precambrian Time	• A massive landmass called Gondwana stretches from pole to pole. North America and Siberia form another landmass, which gradually moves northward. • Cambrian rocks discovered in Canada in 1909 include fossils of shelled creatures and sponges.	• Modern North America turns through 90 degrees and is joined to Greenland to make up the northern landmass of Laurasia. Gondwana lies to the south. • Fish evolve and corals develop on shallow seabeds, building reefs.	• Gondwana slides toward South Pole. • First land plants appear. • Simple animals, such as worms, and millepedes, become established on land.	• The two supercontinents Gondwana and Laurasia edge closer. • Continental plates collide and create mountain chains. • First trees and woodlands appear.	• Frogs and newts evolve rapidly. • First winged insects.	• Remains of trees in swamps to become world's coal supply. •First reptiles evolve.	• A vast single continent called Pang forms. • Much of the land is dese or covered in ice sheets. •Conifers, such as pine trees, appea
Millions of years ago		570	505	438	408	360	320	286

• Precambrian time dates back to the formation of Earth and represents 90 percent of the planet's history.

• During this time, Earth formed into a compact mass and its crust cooled and hardened.

• At the beginning of Precambrian time, conditions on Earth were too hostile for life.

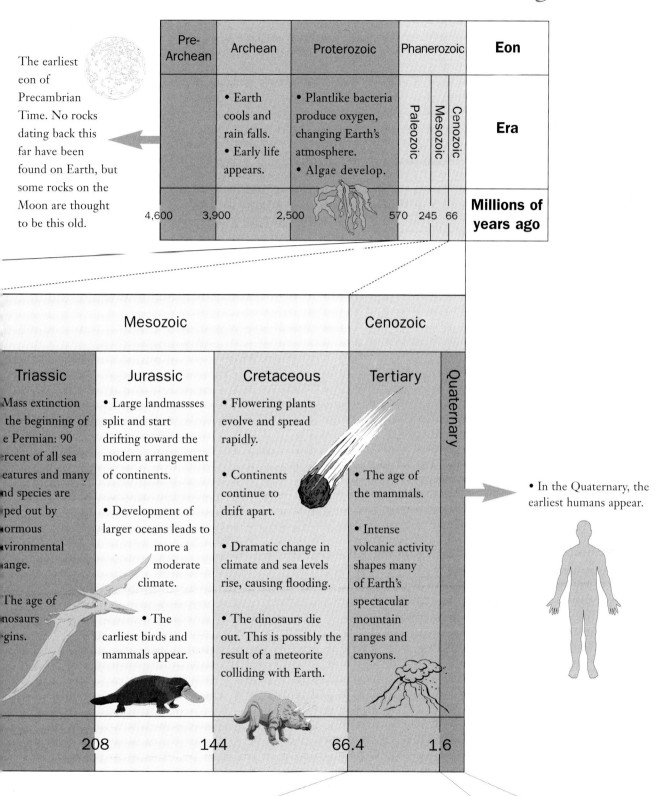

The earliest eon of Precambrian Time. No rocks dating back this far have been found on Earth, but some rocks on the Moon are thought to be this old.

Pre-Archean	Archean	Proterozoic	Phanerozoic				Eon
	• Earth cools and rain falls. • Early life appears.	• Plantlike bacteria produce oxygen, changing Earth's atmosphere. • Algae develop.	Paleozoic	Mesozoic	Cenozoic		Era
4,600	3,900	2,500	570	245	66		Millions of years ago

Mesozoic

Cenozoic

Triassic

• Mass extinction at the beginning of the Permian: 90 percent of all sea creatures and many land species are wiped out by enormous environmental change.

• The age of dinosaurs begins.

Jurassic

• Large landmassses split and start drifting toward the modern arrangement of continents.

• Development of larger oceans leads to more a moderate climate.

• The earliest birds and mammals appear.

Cretaceous

• Flowering plants evolve and spread rapidly.

• Continents continue to drift apart.

• Dramatic change in climate and sea levels rise, causing flooding.

• The dinosaurs die out. This is possibly the result of a meteorite colliding with Earth.

Tertiary

• The age of the mammals.

• Intense volcanic activity shapes many of Earth's spectacular mountain ranges and canyons.

Quaternary

• In the Quaternary, the earliest humans appear.

208	144	66.4	1.6

Paleocene	Eocene	Oligocene	Miocene	Pliocene	Pleistocene	Holocene	Epoch
66.4	57.8	36.6	23.7	5.3	1.6	0.01	Millions of years ago

Science Time Line

C. 3000 B.C.E. People study the Sun and other stars. Stonehenge in England is built to mark where the Sun rises and sets at different points in the year.

600 B.C.E. Greek philosopher Thales of Miletus creates a charge that can pick up a feather by rubbing amber with fur. This is static electricity.

5th century B.C.E. In Mesopotamia, early stargazers make star maps and try to predict the future from the movement of the stars.

460–370 B.C.E. Greek scientist Democritus suggests that all matter is made up of particles called atoms.

1705 Using Newton's ideas about gravity, English astronomer Edmond Halley realizes that the comets seen in 1531, 1607, and 1682 are the same comet. Halley's comet is seen again, as he predicts, in 1758.

1687 English scientist Isaac Newton publishes the *Principia*. It describes how gravity keeps the planets in orbit around the Sun.

1620 English philosopher Francis Bacon points out that South America and Africa would fit together. This suggests the two were once joined.

1610 Invention of the telescope. Galileo builds his own and spots Jupiter's moons. The moons show that not every object in space revolves around Earth.

1781 German-born atronomers William Herschel and his sister Caroline discover the planet Uranus using a giant, home-made telescope.

1803 English scientist John Dalton identifies 33 elements. He also explains how chemical reactions take place through the exchange of atoms.

1840s English scientist James Joule shows how energy can be converted from one form into another. He builds a paddle wheel that heats the water slightly.

1831–1875 Scottish scientist James Clerk Maxwell suggests that visible light is one of many types of electromagnetic radiation, all traveling at the speed of light.

1930 Pluto, the most distant planet in Earth's Solar System, is discovered.

1927 Belgian astronomer Georges Lemaître proposes that the Universe was once packed into a tiny point that exploded in the Big Bang and is still expanding.

1923 U.S. astronomer Edwin Hubble discovers far-off galaxies. He notices that their stars appear red. This "redshift" shows galaxies are moving away from us.

1919 Einstein's theory that light is affected by gravity is proved during a solar eclipse. Scientists observe the deflection of a distant star's light near the Sun.

1934 U.S. naturalist Charles William Beebe develops a spherical diving vessel called the bathysphere and plunges to a record depth of 3,028 feet (923 m). This invention leads to greater knowledge of the ocean depths.

1939–1945 During World War II, U.S. physicists build nuclear bombs. When dropped on Japanese cities Hiroshima and Nagasaki in 1945, they kill 240,000 people.

1960 First U.S. weather satellite is launched. It is named *TIROS* for *T*elevision and *I*nfrared *O*bservation *S*atellite.

1963 The USSR launches the first human, Yuri Gagarin, into space, winning the first leg of the space race. U.S. astronauts land on the Moon in 1969.

384–322 B.C.E. Greek philosopher Aristotle teaches that the Universe is made up of mixtures of elements: air, earth, fire, water, and ether.

200 B.C.E. Greek astronomer Eratosthenes decides the Earth is shaped like a ball with a circumference of 25,000 miles (40,233 km). This figure was only 200 km off.

150 C.E. Alexandrian astronomer Ptolemy makes a model of the Universe in which the Moon, Sun, and planets revolve around Earth.

1492 Believing the Earth is a ball, Italian explorer Christopher Columbus sets sail west from Spain, aiming to reach Asia. Instead, he reaches the Americas, which lie in the way.

1589 Italian scientist Galileo Galilei shows that all objects are pulled to Earth at the same rate. He drops a heavy and a light object from the top of the Leaning Tower of Pisa.

1582 Pope Gregory XIII has a new calendar drawn up. The Gregorian calendar varies from the true solar year by only 26 seconds.

1543 Polish monk Nicolaus Copernicus introduces the idea that the planets revolve around the Sun, not around the Earth.

1519–1522 Portuguese explorer Ferdinand Magellan circumnavigates (sails around) the globe, proving that the Earth is spherical.

1830s Swiss geologist Louis Agassiz studies rock features in northern Europe and North America. He finds that vast areas were once covered by ice.

1896 French physicist Antoine Henri Becquerel discovers that uranium gives out strong radiation. Polish scientist Marie Curie further investigates this radioactivity.

1897 English physicist J. J. Thomson discovers the electron. He believes an atom is built like a plum pudding, with negative electrons dotted through a positive mass.

1905 German-born U.S. scientist Albert Einstein explains how a very small amount of matter can be converted into a huge amount of energy. This led to the generation of energy by nuclear fission and fusion. $E = mc^2$

1915 German-born U.S. physicist Albert Einstein writes the general theory of relativity. He suggests that gravity is caused by a large mass distorting space and time.

1913 Danish chemist Niels Bohr devises a model of the atom with electrons orbiting the nucleus in different energy levels.

1912 Austrian-born U.S. scientist Victor Hess flies in a hot-air balloon to measure radiation reaching Earth from space. He finds that Earth is bombarded by cosmic rays.

1911 New Zealand-born physicist Ernest Rutherford discovers the nucleus of the atom when he fires particles at a sheet of gold. A few particles bounce back when they hit the gold atoms' nuclei.

1973 U.S. chemists begin to study the effects of chlorofluorocarbons (CFCs) on the atmosphere. In the 1980s satellite images reveal a hole in the ozone layer.

1986 A reactor explodes at a nuclear power plant in Chernobyl, Ukraine. This causes protests about the use of nuclear power.

1990 Hubble Space Telescope is launched. It looks into the depths of space and makes hundreds of discoveries, including black holes.

2001 and beyond The International Space Station, crewed by scientists and astronauts, acts as an orbiting laboratory and docking station for further space exploration.

Periodic Table

The periodic table classifies chemical elements according to their properties and increasing atomic weight. The first element in the table is therefore hydrogen, the lightest element. There are currently at least 118 known elements. However, some of these have existed only for a short space of time in the laboratory. The most recently produced elements (110 to 112, 114, 116, and 118) have not yet been officially named.

The metals in the **transition series** share similar properties. As with all elements, their chemical properties result from the electron structure of their atoms. However, ions of these metals can hold a varying number of electrons and can therefore make many different compounds, with several vibrant colors.

Metals

An opaque, shiny substance that is a good conductor of electricity and heat.

Metalloid

A substance that is half metal, half nonmetal. Many are semiconductors that can stop and start a current of electricity.

Nonmetal

Element that does not share the properties of metals. Nonmetals readily gain electrons to form negative ions and they are poor conductors of heat and electricity.

Hydrogen is the first element in the first group of the table. More than 90% of atoms in the Universe are hydrogen. Under usual conditions, hydrogen exists as a diatomic molecule (H_2)—a very light, explosive gas.

Transition series

Periods

1	2		3	4	5	6	7
1 **H** hydrogen							
3 **Li** lithium	4 **Be** beryllium						
11 **Na** sodium	12 **Mg** magnesium						
19 **K** potassium	20 **Ca** calcium		21 **Sc** scandium	22 **Ti** titanium	23 **V** vanadium	24 **Cr** chromium	2 **M** manga
37 **Rb** rubidium	38 **Sr** strontium		39 **Y** yttrium	40 **Zr** zirconium	41 **Nb** niobium	42 **Mo** molybdenum	4 **Tc** techn
55 **Cs** caesium	56 **Ba** barium	57-70 *	71 **Lu** lutetium	72 **Hf** hafnium	73 **Ta** tantalum	74 **W** tungsten	7 **R** rher
87 **Fr** francium	88 **Ra** radium	89-102 †	103 **Lr** lawrencium	104 **Rf** rutherfordium	105 **Db** dubnium	106 **Sg** seaborgium	10 **B** bohr

The **alkali metals** are in Group 1 of the table. They include highly reactive metals such as sodium and potassium. These metals readily react with acids and they are mainly found in nature as ionic salt compounds.

Lanthanide series *

57 **La** lanthanum	58 **Ce** cerium	59 **Pr** praseodymium	60 **Nd** neodymium	6 **P** prome

Actinide series †

89 **Ac** actinium	90 **Th** thorium	91 **Pa** protactinium	92 **U** uranium	9 **N** neptu

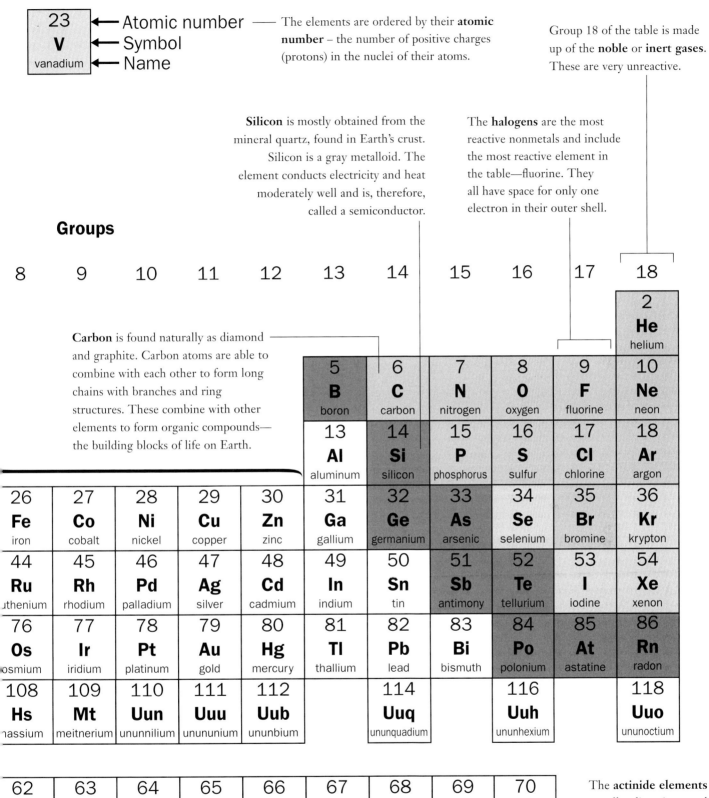

23
V
vanadium

← Atomic number
← Symbol
← Name

The elements are ordered by their **atomic number** – the number of positive charges (protons) in the nuclei of their atoms.

Group 18 of the table is made up of the **noble** or **inert gases**. These are very unreactive.

Silicon is mostly obtained from the mineral quartz, found in Earth's crust. Silicon is a gray metalloid. The element conducts electricity and heat moderately well and is, therefore, called a semiconductor.

The **halogens** are the most reactive nonmetals and include the most reactive element in the table—fluorine. They all have space for only one electron in their outer shell.

Carbon is found naturally as diamond and graphite. Carbon atoms are able to combine with each other to form long chains with branches and ring structures. These combine with other elements to form organic compounds—the building blocks of life on Earth.

The **actinide elements** are all radioactive metals. Uranium was discovered first, in 1789, and was named for the recently-spotted planet, Uranus.

Groups

8	9	10	11	12	13	14	15	16	17	18
										2 **He** helium
					5 **B** boron	6 **C** carbon	7 **N** nitrogen	8 **O** oxygen	9 **F** fluorine	10 **Ne** neon
					13 **Al** aluminum	14 **Si** silicon	15 **P** phosphorus	16 **S** sulfur	17 **Cl** chlorine	18 **Ar** argon
26 **Fe** iron	27 **Co** cobalt	28 **Ni** nickel	29 **Cu** copper	30 **Zn** zinc	31 **Ga** gallium	32 **Ge** germanium	33 **As** arsenic	34 **Se** selenium	35 **Br** bromine	36 **Kr** krypton
44 **Ru** ruthenium	45 **Rh** rhodium	46 **Pd** palladium	47 **Ag** silver	48 **Cd** cadmium	49 **In** indium	50 **Sn** tin	51 **Sb** antimony	52 **Te** tellurium	53 **I** iodine	54 **Xe** xenon
76 **Os** osmium	77 **Ir** iridium	78 **Pt** platinum	79 **Au** gold	80 **Hg** mercury	81 **Tl** thallium	82 **Pb** lead	83 **Bi** bismuth	84 **Po** polonium	85 **At** astatine	86 **Rn** radon
108 **Hs** hassium	109 **Mt** meitnerium	110 **Uun** ununnilium	111 **Uuu** unununium	112 **Uub** ununbium		114 **Uuq** ununquadium		116 **Uuh** ununhexium		118 **Uuo** ununoctium

62 **Sm** samarium	63 **Eu** europium	64 **Gd** gadolinium	65 **Tb** terbium	66 **Dy** dysprosium	67 **Ho** holmium	68 **Er** erbium	69 **Tm** thulium	70 **Yb** ytterbium
94 **Pu** plutonium	95 **Am** americium	96 **Cm** curium	97 **Bk** berkelium	98 **Cf** californium	99 **Es** einsteinium	100 **Fm** fermium	101 **Md** mendelevium	102 **No** nobelium

Places to Go

PLACES TO GO BY STATE

Alabama
U.S. Space and Rocket Center
☎ (800) 637-7223
http://www.ussrc.com

Alaska
Alaska Museum of Natural History
☎ (907) 694-0819
http://www.alaskamuseum.org

Arizona
Grand Canyon National Park
☎ (520) 638-7888
http://www.grand.canyon.national-park.com

Arkansas
Arkansas Museum of Natural Resources
☎ (870) 725-2877
http://www.cei.net/~amnr

California
Orange County Natural History Museum
☎ (800) 417-3529
http://www.ocnha.mus.ca.us

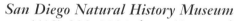
San Diego Natural History Museum
☎ (619) 232-3821 http://www.sdnhm.org

Colorado
The Wings Over the Rockies Air and Space Museum
☎ (303) 360-5360
http://www.dimensional.com/~worm/

Connecticut
Dinosaur State Park
☎ (860) 529-8423
http://www.dinosaurstatepark.org

Florida
Kennedy Space Center
☎ (321) 452-2121
http://www.kennedyspacecenter.com

Tallahassee Museum
☎ (850) 576-1636
http://www.tallahasseemuseum.org

Georgia
West Georgia Museum of Tallapoosa
☎ (404) 574-3125

Hawaii
Iao Valley, Maui
☎ (800) 525-6284

Illinois
The Field Museum
☎ (312) 922-9410 http://www.fmnh.org

Indiana
Indiana State Museum
☎ (317) 232-1637 http://www.indy.org

Kansas
Natural History Museum and Biodiversity Center, University of Kansas ☎ (785) 864-4450
http://ron.nhm.ukans.edu

Kentucky
Big Bone Licks State Park Museum
☎ (606) 384-3522

Maine
Maine State Museum
☎ (207) 287-2301

Maryland
Maryland Science Center
☎ (410) 685-5225
http://www.mdsci.org

National Museum of Natural History, Smithsonian Institution, Washington, D.C.
☎ (202) 357-2700
http://www.mnh.si.edu

Michigan
Impression 5 Science Center
☎ (517) 485-8116
http://www.claras.com/%21visitlansing3.html

Minnesota
Minneapolis Planetarium
☎ (612) 630-6155

Mississippi
Rainwater Observatory
☎ (662) 547-6865
http://www.rainwater.astronomers.org/info

Montana
Glacier Institute
☎ (406) 888-5215

New Jersey
Liberty Science Center
☎ (201) 200-1000
http://www.lsc.org

The Newark Museum and Dreyfuss Planetarium
☎ (973) 596-6550
http://www.newarkmuseum.org

New York
*American Museum of Natural History
and Rose Center for Earth and Space*
☎ (212) 496-3586
http://www.amnh.org

Petrified Creatures Museum of Natural History
☎ (315) 858-2868

North Carolina
Museum of Natural Sciences
☎ (877) 462-8724
http://www.naturalsciences.org

Ohio
*The Cleveland Museum of
Natural History*
☎ (800) 317-9155
http://www.cmnh.org/info

Oklahoma
*Sam Noble Oklahoma Museum
of Natural History*
☎ (405) 325-4712
http://www.snomnh.ou.edu

Oregon
*Museum of Natural History,
Oregon University*
☎ (503) 346-3024
http://natural-history.uoregon.edu

Pennsylvania
Carnegie Museum of Pittsburgh
☎ (412) 622-3314
http://www.carnegiemuseums.org

Erie Historical Museum and Planetarium
☎ (814) 871-5790
http://www.erie.net/~ehmp/main.html

Rhode Island
*Museum of Natural History
and Planetarium*
☎ (401) 785-9450
http://www.osfn.org/museum/contact.html

Texas
*Brazosport Nature Center and
Planetarium, Center of Arts and Sciences*
☎ (409) 265-3376
http://www.tgn.net/~snark/ncap/ncap.html

Virginia
*The Virginia Museum
of Natural History*
☎ (540) 666-8600
http://www.vmnh.org

Wisconsin
Cable Natural History Museum
☎ (715) 798-3890
http://www.cablemuseum.org

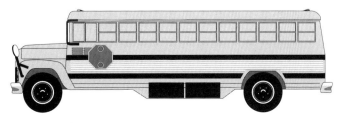

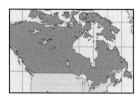

Canada

Aero Space Museum of Calgary
☎ (403) 250-3752
http://www.asmac.ab.ca

The Manitoba Museum of Man and Nature
☎ (204) 956-2830
http://www.manitobamuseum.mb.ca/map.htm

The Miller Museum of Geology, Ontario
☎ (613) 533-6767
http://geol.queensu.ca/museum/museum.html

Nova Scotia Museum of Natural History
☎ (800) 632-1114
http://www.museum.gov.ns.ca/mnh/visit/index.htm

Royal Ontario Museum
☎ (416) 586-8000
http://www.rom.on.ca

NATIONAL PARKS

United States

Acadia National Park, Bar Harbor, ME
Explore the rocky shoreline with a ranger
☎ (207) 288-3338

Arches National Park, near Moab, UT
Sandstone arches and rock faulting
☎ (435) 719-2299

Badlands National Park, southwestern SD
World's richest Oligocene epoch fossil beds
☎ (605) 433-5361

Grand Canyon National Park, AZ
☎ (520) 638-7888

Great Basin National Park, Baker, NV
Includes numerous limestone caverns
☎ (775) 234-7331

Hawaii Volcanoes National Park, HI
☎ (808) 985-6000

Joshua Tree National Park, near Palm Springs, CA
Desert dotted with palm oases
☎ (760) 367-5500

Mammoth Cave National Park, KY
Longest cave system in the world
☎ (270) 758-2251

Redwood National Park, CA
Home to some of the world's tallest trees
☎ (707) 464-6101

Rocky Mountains National Park, Estes Park, CO
Peaks more than 14,000 feet high
☎ (970) 586-1206

Yellowstone National Park, WY
Geysers, hot springs, and fossil forests
☎ (307) 344-7381

Yosemite National Park, CA
Waterfalls and forests with giant sequoias
☎ (209) 372-0200

U.S. National Park Service
http://www.nps.gov

Canada

Banff National Park, Alberta
Mountains, canyons, glaciers, icefields, and hot springs
☎ (403) 762-1550

Glacier National Park, Manitoba
Exposed layers of Precambrian sedimentary rock
☎ (406) 888-7800

Waterton Lakes National Park, Alberta
☎ (403) 859-5133

Yoho National Park, British Colombia
Includes Burgess Shale fossil bed
☎ (250) 343-6783

Things to Do

BOOKS

Biomes of the World series
(Marshall Cavendish, 1996, $18)

A City Under the Sea: Life in a Coral Reef
by Norbert Wu
(Atheneum, 1996, $11.20)

Earth and Space
(Starting Point Science series)
by Susan Mayes and Sophy Tahta
(EDC Publications, 1995, $17.95)

The Earth in Space:
Straightforward Science
by Peter D. Riley
(Franklin Watts, 1999, $20)

Earth: The Making of a Planet
by Roy Gallant
(Marshall Cavendish, 1998, $19.95)

The Elements series
(Marshall Cavendish, 2000, $16)

Geology Rocks: 50 Hands-on Activities
to Explore the Earth
by Cindy Blobaum
(Williamson Publishing, 1999, $10.95)

Geysers: When Earth Roars
by Roy Gallant
(Franklin Watts, 1997, $22.50)

How? More Experiments
for the Young Scientist
by Dave and Kathy Prochnow
(TAB Books, 1993, $11)

Life in Deserts
by Lucy Baker
(World Book Ecology series, 1997, $5.95)

The Living Ocean
by Elizabeth Collins
(Earth at Risk, 1994, $19.95)

Night Sky Guide
by the editors of Sky & Telescope
(Sky Publishing Group, $12.95)

Nightwatch: A Practical Guide to
Viewing the Universe, 3rd edition
by Terence Dickinson
(Sky Publishing Group, 1998, $29.95)

Sir Isaac Newton: Discovering Laws
That Govern the Universe
by E. N. Andrade
(Blackbirch Press, 1999, $18.95)

The Story of Science series
(Marshall Cavendish, 2000, $29.95)

When the Sun Dies
by Roy Gallant
(Marshall Cavendish, 1998, $19.95)

The Young Astronomers
by Harry Ford
(DK Publishing, 1998, $15.95)

MAGAZINES/ORGANIZATIONS

Astronomy
☎ (800) 533-6644
http://www.astronomy.com

Explore Magazine
P.O. Box 37588
Boone, IA 50037-4588
☎ (877) 817-4395
http://www.exploremagazine.com

Muse
Smithsonian Institution
P.O. Box 7468
Red Oak, IA 51591-2468

Odyssey
Cousteau Society
930 W. 21st Street
Norfolk, VA 23517
☎ (804) 627-1144
http://www.odysseymagazine.com

Science News
P.O. Box 1925
Marion, OH 43305
☎ (800) 552-4412

REFERENCE WORKS

Aquatic Life of the World
(Marshall Cavendish, 2000, $459.95)

Biographical Encyclopedia of Scientists
edited by Richard Olsen
(Marshall Cavendish, 1998, $339.95)

Dinosaurs of the World
(Marshall Cavendish, 1999, $495.95)

Elements
(Grolier, $305.00)

Encyclopedia of Paleontology
(Fitzroy Dearborn, 1998, $442.50)

Innovations in Earth Sciences
(ABC-CLIO, $50.00)

CLUBS

American Hiking Society
1015 31st Street N.W.
Washington, D.C. 20007
☎ (703) 385-3252

American Rivers
801 Pennsylvania Avenue, S.E.
Suite 400
Washington, D.C., 20003
☎ (202) 547-6900
(Volunteer river cleanups)

Denver Museum of Natural History
2001 Colorado Boulevard
Denver, CO 80205-5798
☎ (303) 370-6304
(Weekend family outings)

INTERNET RESOURCES

Bill Nye the Science Guy's Nye Labs Online
http://www.nyelabs.com/flash_go.html

Ecology and Biodiversity
http://www.conbio.rice.edu/VL

National Oceanic and Atmospheric Administration (NOAA)
http://www.noaa.gov

El Niño: Southern Oscillation (ENSO) Homepage
http://www.ogp.noaa.gov

National Aeronautics and Space Administration (NASA)
http://www.nasa.gov

JSC Imagery Services
http://images.jsc.nasa.gov

Lunar Prospector Mission
http://lunar.arc.nasa.gov

SeaWiFS Project
http://seawifs.gsfc.nasa.gov

The Particle Adventure
The fundamentals of matter and forces
http://www.particleadventure.org

National Aquarium in Baltimore
http://www.aqua.org

Smithsonian Institution: Site for Kids
http://www.kidscastle.si.edu

United States Environmental Protection Agency
http://www.epa.gov

United States Geological Survey (USGS)
http://www.usgs.gov

Discovery Channel Network
http://dsc.discovery.com

SPACE CAMPS

U.S. Spacecamp/ Aviation Challenge Reservations
P.O. Box 070015
Huntsville AL 35807-7015
☎ (800) 533-7281

For other locations in the United States:
http://www.spacecamp.com

Space Camp Canada
Canadian Space Resource Center
2150 Laurentian Autoroute
Laval, Quebec H7T 2T8
Canada
☎ (514) 978-3600
http://www.cosmodome.org

Glossary

abrasive (uh-BRAY-siv) Substance used to smooth or polish another.

absorb To suck or draw in. Also, to receive sound or light without reflecting it.

acid rain Rain polluted by sulfur and nitrogen oxide emissions from burning coal and oil.

airstream Flow of air around a flying object, such as an airplane.

algae (AL-jee) Seaweed and other, mostly marine, plantlike organisms.

alkali (AL-kuh-ly) Salt that forms a solution in water with a pH level greater than 7. pH is a measure of acidity or alkalinity.

allergic reaction Unpleasant physical response to a substance.

altitude Height above sea level.

ammonia (uh-MOH-nee-uh) Pungent, colorless gas; a compound of nitrogen and hydrogen.

ammonite (A-muh-nyt) Extinct marine mollusk with a coiled shell.

amphibian (am-FIH-bee-uhnz) Cold-blooded animal adapted to live both on land and in the water, such as a toad or salamander.

analog Showing data with a moving pointer or clock hands. *See also* digital.

ancestor (AN-SEHS-tuhr) Individual who lived long before another member of the same family. *See also* descendant.

antiparticle Subatomic particle identical to another in mass, but with an opposite charge.

aperture (AP-uhr-CHOOR) Opening.

aquifer (AK-wuh-fuhr) Water-bearing layer of rock.

asbestos (as-BES-tuhs) Mineral whose fibers were used as insulating material until it was found they caused some cancers.

atoll (A-tawl) Roughly ring-shaped coral island.

atom bomb Bomb with huge explosive power created by nuclear fission.

atomic mass The mass of an atom, usually expressed in atomic mass units.

atomic number Number that determines an element's chemical properties and where it is in the periodic table.

aureole (AWR-ee-OHL) Glowing ring around a bright object such as the Sun.

axis (AK-suhs) Imaginary line through a planet around which the planet revolves.

axle (AK-suhl) Rod joining a pair of wheels.

bait (BAYT) Something used to attract an animal into a trap, or a fish onto a hook.

bellows Instrument that puffs out a blast of air; used to help combustion (burning).

binary numbers Number system using only zeros and ones.

blast furnace Heater in which a blast of air helps a substance to burn. Used to refine iron ore.

blizzard Long, severe snowstorm or a strong, snowy wind.

blood type Composition of a person's blood. There are four blood types: A, B, AB, and O.

breeder reactor Type of nuclear reactor that generates energy by fission (splitting nuclei). It produces more fissionable material than it uses as fuel. *See also* nuclear reactor.

brittle (BRIH-tuhl) Easily snapped or cracked.

broadcast To transmit sound or images by radio or television.

by-product Something produced by an industrial or biological process; not the main product.

cellulose (SEL-yuh-LOHZ) Complex molecule that strengthens the cell walls in plants.

center of gravity Point in a three-dimensional object. If the object is supported here, it will balance.

chain reaction Series of events in which one triggers the next.

chemical analysis Investigating the chemical makeup of a substance.

coal seam Layer of coal between layers of rock.

colony Group of individuals of one species living together.

complex Having many interrelated parts.

compress To squeeze a substance so that it takes up less room.

concave (kahn-KAYV) Hollowed in the center. *See also* convex.

conductor Material that allows electricity or heat to flow through it. *See also* insulator.

contaminate To introduce an unwanted or harmful substance into something.

continental plate Section of Earth's crust that carries a landmass. *See also* oceanic plate.

continental shield Large, stable area of low relief in Earth's crust. Each of Earth's continents has a continental shield.

convection (kuhn-VEK-shuhn) Transfering heat in a circular motion through liquid and gas.

convex (kahn-VEKS) Bulging in the center. *See also* concave.

core Center of an object.

corona (kuh-ROH-nuh) Halo around a luminous object.

corrosion Process of wearing away by chemical action.

counterbalance To offset a weight with an object of the same weight.

covalent bond Chemical bond between atoms, made by sharing electrons.

cracking Process by which heavy hydrocarbon molecules in crude oil are broken up by heat and pressure to make lighter products such as gasoline.

crude oil Oil in its natural state.

crustacean (KRUHS-TAY-shuhn) Shelled animal such as a crab.

culture (KUHL-chuhr) Sample of living material grown in a prepared nutrient-rich substance.

data (DAY-tuh) Series of facts, measurements, or calculations.

decimal numbers Number system that uses ten digits: zero through nine.

decompose To decay and separate into parts.

deflect (dih-FLEKT) To turn something off its course.

descendant (dih-SEN-duhnt) Individual who lives long after another member of the same family. *See also* ancestor.

detonator (DEH-tuh-NAY-tuhr) Device used to set off (detonate) an explosive.

diameter (dy-A-muh-tuhr) Length of a line between two points on a circle, which also passes through the circle's center.

diffuse (dih-FYOO-shuhn) How particles of gas or liquid move randomly and spread out.

digital Representing data in the form of numbers. *See also* analog.

diode (DY-ohd) Electronic device with two terminals; used to make current flow in one direction.

displacement (dih-SPLAY-smuhnt) Measurement of the movement of an object or substance.

distillation (DIS-tuh-LAY-shuhn) Process of purifying a liquid by evaporating and condensing it.

domains (doh-MAYNZ) Small areas of magnetization in a ferromagnetic (easily magnetized) substance.

dormant Showing no signs of activity for a time.

echinoderms (ih-KY-nuh-DUHRMZ) Group of marine animals with radial symmetry, including starfish, sand dollars, and sea urchins.

eclipse (ih-KLIPS) When one celestial object obscures another.

ecliptic (ih-KLIP-tik) Circular path along which the Sun appears to move during the year.

eddy (EH-dee) Current of water or air that runs against the flow.

electromagnet Magnet created by passing an electric current through a wire surrounding a core of magnetic material.

elliptical (ih-LIP-tih-kuhl) Oval.

engineer (EN-juh-NEER) Person who designs mechanical, structural, and electrical devices.

entropy (EN-truh-pee) Disordered state of molecules, which increases as an object ages.

epicenter (EH-puh-SEN-tuhr) Part of Earth's surface above the place of origin of an earthquake.

evaporation (ih-VA-puh-RAY-shuhn) When a liquid turns into a gas.

evolution (EH-vuh-LOO-shuhn) How living organisms adapt over millions of years to changes in their environment.

exhaust (ek-ZAWST) Discharge of used fluid or vapor from an engine.

extract To separate something from a mixture.

extraterrestrial Not from Earth.

fatty acids Group of acids, many of which occur naturally in fats.

fault (FAWLT) Fracture in Earth's crust causing the displacement of the crust on one side.

fermentation (FUHR-muhn-TAY-shuhn) Chemical change producing fizz.

fertile Able to support life or produce offspring.

fiber (FY-buhr) Thread or a thread-shaped object.

fiberglass Strong, light material made from glass fibers and plastic.

filament Thread of a conducting material that glows when an electric current passes through it.

filter To separate out fine solids from liquids or gas. Used in purification processes.

fissure (FIH-shuhr) Long crack.

fjord (fee-AWRD) Inlet of the sea between cliffs or steep slopes; formed by glacier erosion.

flammable Easily ignited (set on fire); burns quickly.

flight controller Someone who controls an airplane or spacecraft flight by signals from the ground.

flood tide Rising tide. *See also* ebb tide.

floodplain Level land that may be flooded if a river bursts its banks.

focal length The distance between a lens and an image of a far off object it has brought into focus.

food additives Chemicals used in processed food to enhance their color or taste.

food chain The order of organisms in a community, whereby each depends on another as its food source.

forensic science The use of science to investigate crimes.

fossil fuel (FAH-suhl FYOO-uhl) Fuel such as coal, natural gas, or oil, which formed from plant and animal remains.

free radicals Groups of atoms that can exist freely for a short time.

friction (FRIK-shuhn) Force that slows the movement of two objects in contact.

fulcrum (FUL-krum) Fixed point on which a lever turns.

fungi (FUN-gee) Organisms such as molds and mushrooms, which live off decaying organic remains.

galvanize (GAL-vuh-nyz) To coat with zinc.

gamma rays Photons emitted by a radioactive substance. Part of the electromagnetic spectrum.

gas giants Four large planets in the Solar System: Jupiter, Saturn, Uranus, and Neptune; so named because they are mostly gas.

gear Toothed wheel that is part of a larger piece of machinery.

gene (JEEN) Strand of DNA that codes for a biological molecule.

generator Machine that transforms mechanical energy into electricity.

genus (JEH-nuhs) Group made up of a number of closely related species.

gill Organ (as of a fish) used to obtain oxygen from water.

graphite (GRA-fyt) Soft, black form of carbon.

graptolite (GRAP-tuh-lyt) Small, extinct, water-dwelling animals.

gyroscope (JY-ruh-SKOHP) Wheel with a rod through its center, mounted so that both turn freely.

hard water Water containing calcium and magnesium ions; does not lather easily with soap.

headwaters The part of a river near its source.

hemisphere (HEH-muh-SFIR) Half of a ball-shaped object.

hibernate (HY-buhr-NAYT) To sleep for winter to conserve energy while food is scarce.

horizon (huh-RY-zuhn) Apparent boundary between the sky and the land or sea.

hormone Chemicals produced in the body that have specific effects on certain cell activity.

hot spot Point where hot magma inside Earth melts through the crust, forming volcanic features.

hull Shell of a boat or ship.

hyperbola (hy-PUHR-buh-luh) Type of U-shaped curve.

ice cap All-year-round covering of ice and snow.

icebreaker Ship with a strong hull to break through sea ice.

impervious (im-PUHR-vee-uhs) Not allowing anything in.

impurities (im-PYOOR-uh-teez) Unwanted substances present in a mineral, which are removed to obtain a pure element.

industrialized world Part of the world where more people work in industry and manufacturing than in farming. Broadly, Europe and North America.

inert gases Group of rare gases that includes helium and neon; very stable and never react.

inertia (ih-NUHR-shuh) State an object is in when no outside force is acting upon it.

infinite (IN-fuh-nuht) Having no end or limit.

insulator (IN-suh-LAY-tuhr) A poor conductor of electricity and heat. *See also* conductor.

interglacial period Period when most of Earth's surface is free of year-round ice.

internal combustion engine Engine in which fuel is combusted (burned) inside the engine itself.

inversely proportional The relationship between two quantities, in which one gets bigger as the other gets smaller.

invertebrate (IN-VUHR-tuh-bruht) Animal with no backbone.

irrigate To water by underground pipes, sprinklers or airplane.

kinetic energy Energy of motion.

lagoon (luh-GOON) Shallow pond or channel that is part of a larger body of water.

landfill Hole dug in the earth, filled with waste and covered.

landslide Rapid movement of rock or soil down a steep slope.

lattice (LA-tuhs) Regular arrangement, such as that of atoms in a crystal.

launch vehicle Rocket used to launch (send into orbit) a satellite or spacecraft. It stays on the ground at takeoff.

leeward Facing in the direction that the prevailing wind blows.

lens Piece of transparent material used to focus rays of light.

levee (LEH-vee) Bank of sediment deposited by a river.

lichen (LY-kuhn) Plant made up of a fungus and an alga.

light-year Distance light travels in a year through a vacuum (5.88 trillion miles or 9.46 trillion kilometers).

loch Gaelic word meaning "lake."

longsighted Unable to see nearby objects clearly.

lubricate To reduce friction between moving parts of machinery by applying a substance such as oil (called a lubricant).

lunar (LOO-nuhr) Involving the Moon. *See also* solar.

luster Shininess.

magnetic field Area around a magnetic object in which its magnetic forces can act.

magnetosphere Area around a large object in space that is dominated by the object's magnetic field.

magnitude Size or quality; also, the brightness of a star.

mantle Layer beneath Earth's crust.

marine biologist Scientist who studies the organisms that live in the sea.

medium (MEE-dee-um) Material through which energy travels.

meltdown The accidental melting of the core of a nuclear reactor, releasing radioactivity.

meridian Imaginary circle on the surface of Earth that passes through the poles.

metabolize (muh-TA-buh-LYZ) The way that cells convert a substance by chemical changes in order to use it for life processes.

metallic Containing a metal or having the properties of a metal.

meteor (MEE-tee-or) Effect seen from Earth when a meteoroid burns up in Earth's atmosphere.

meteorite (MEE-tee-uh-RYT) Meteoriod that reaches Earth's surface.

meteoroid (MEE-tee-uh-ROYD) Rock particle in orbit around the Sun.

Middle East The countries of southwest Asia and northeast Africa, from Libya in the west to Afghanistan in the east.

midlatitudes Temperate regions between 30 and 60 degrees north and south of the equator.

migrate (MY-grayt) To move to another climate or region for breeding or to find food.

mollusk (MAH-luhsk) spineless animal with a soft, muscular body and often enclosed in a hard shell, such as a snail, clam, or squid.

momentum Force gained by motion; measured by the length of time needed to bring the object to rest.

moraines (muh-RAYNZ) Clusters of earth and stones carried and deposited by a glacier.

mortar (MAWR-tuhr) Building material that is a mixture of cement, lime, sand, and water.

motor Machine that powers movement.

mountain building Gradual process whereby Earth's plates collide, folding Earth's crust.

mudflat Level area of land under shallow waters. Also, land covered and uncovered by the tide.

naked eye Unaided vision—not using a telescope or binoculars.

nautilus (NAW-tuh-luhs) Mollusks of the South Pacific and Indian Oceans with spiral shells that have pearly insides.

navigable (NA-vuh-guh-buhl) Body of water deep and wide enough to allow ships through.

nervous system System in vertebrates made up of the brain, spinal cord, and nerves; how the body receives and responds to outside stimuli.

North Star The star seen in the sky of the Northern Hemisphere toward which Earth's axis points. Used by navigators.

nuclear reactor Device for the controlled release of nuclear energy. *See also* breeder reactor.

nutrient (NOO-tree-uhnt) Food necessary for an organism's life processes.

oasis (oh-AY-suhs) Fertile area in a desert or other barren region.

observatory (ub-ZUHR-vuh-TOH-ree) Building containing equipment for making astronomical observations.

oceanic plate Section of Earth's crust that carries a body of water. *See also* continental plate.

organic Containing carbon and hydrogen.

overfishing Harvesting seafood until the stock is threatened.

pampas (PAM-puhz) Large, grassy plains of temperate South America east of the Andes.

pancreas (PAN-kree-uhs) Large gland in the body of back-boned animals that makes enzymes needed for digestion and the hormones insulin and glucagon.

parabola (puh-RA-buh-luh) U-shaped curve; the shape of a plane cutting through a cone at a certain angle.

parallax Difference in apparent direction of an object as seen from two points that are far apart.

parallel Lines running in the same direction, an equal distance apart along their entire length.

paralysis (puh-RAH-luh-suhs) Inability to move.

patent (PA-tuhnt) Official document showing ownership of an idea or invention.

payload The cargo carried by a spacecraft.

pendulum (PEN-juh-luhm) Suspended object that swings freely to and fro.

peninsula Piece of land jutting out into the water.

periscope (PEH-ruh-SKOHP) Instrument containing lenses and mirrors that allows somebody to see around obstacles.

pharmacologist (FAHR-muh-KAH-luh-jist) Chemist involved in creating new medical drugs.

phase (FAYZ) Appearance of a planet or moon from Earth.

photon (FOH-tahn) Packet of light energy.

pitch Highness or lowness of sound.

pivot (PIH-vuht) Pin on which something turns or balances.

plate boundary Area where two plates of Earth's crust meet.

polarize (POH-luh-RYZ) To break into groups that repel one another.

pollutant (puh-LOO-tuhnt) Harmful substance released into the environment.

porous (PAW-ruhs) Full of pores (tiny channels). A porous rock allows water to seep into it.

prairies (PREHR-eez) Large areas of flattish grassland.

precipitation (pri-SIH-puh-TAY-shuhn) Water falling from clouds as rain, sleet, snow, or hail.

predator Animal that kills and eats other animals.

primates (PRY-mayts) Group of mammals that includes apes, monkeys, and lemurs.

proportion How much of the whole a particular part takes up.

pulley Rope over a grooved wheel used to help lift heavy objects.

quark (KWAWRK) Subatomic particle thought to exist in pairs. *See also* subatomic particles.

quarrying (KWOH-ree-ing) Extracting material such as building stone, slate, or limestone from a site (called a quarry).

radiation Process of emitting radiant energy in the form of waves or particles.

radioactive decay Disintegration of the nucleus of a radioactive atom or isotope.

radiotherapy Medical treatment that uses radiation.

radius Half a circle's diameter. *See also* diameter.

random Having no pattern.

ratio (RAY-shoh) Relationship in size or amount between two or more things.

recycled Made from already used material.

refinery (rih-FY-nuh-ree) Building or equipment for refining or processing oil.

refraction (rih-FRAK-shuhn) Apparent bending of light as it passes from one medium to another.

reptiles Air-breathing, back-boned animals with scaly bodies. They crawl on their bellies (e.g., snakes) or on stubby legs (e.g., lizards).

reservoir (REH-zuhr-vwahr) Stored supply, for example, of water. Often a humanmade lake.

residue (REH-zuh-DOO) Material left behind.

resinous (REH-zuh-nuhs) Having the properties of resin (a sticky, yellowish sap secreted by plants).

resonance (REH-zuh-nuhnts) Vibration of large amplitude that creates a rich sound.

river basin Area of land drained by a river and its branches.

rocket booster First stage of a multistage rocket that provides thrust for the launch and initial part of the flight.

runoff Snow and rainfall that eventually runs into a river.

saturate (SA-chuh-RAYT) To fill with a substance until no more can be taken in.

sediment Material dropped by water, wind, or glaciers.

seismic (SYZ-mik) Subject to, or caused by, an earthquake.

sewage (SOO-ij) Waste liquids or matter carried off in sewers.

shale Type of rock formed by the consolidation of clay, mud, or silt.

shock wave Compressed wave (e.g., of sound) caused by a disturbance such as an explosion or an earthquake.

short circuit Point of low resistance in a circuit that allows more power to flow. This can damage the circuit elsewhere.

shortsighted Unable to see distant objects clearly.

silicon chip Wafer of silicon (a semiconductor) that is the main part in an electric circuit.

sill Underwater ridge separating the beds of two bodies of water.

silt Fine-grained deposit in the water. *See also* deposit.

smog Dark, heavy fog formed when smoke and chemical fumes are present in the atmosphere.

solar Involving the Sun. *See also* lunar.

solar panel Sheet made up of cells that convert sunlight into electrical energy.

solvent Substance (usually liquid), which dissolves a solid to form a solution.

space walk Excursion outside the spacecraft by an astronaut.

species (SPEE-sheez) Large group of organisms with common characteristics.

splash down When a crewed spacecraft arriving back on Earth splashes into the ocean.

static electricity Electricity produced by on-off, nonmoving charges. For example, those produced by friction.

sterilize (STEHR-uh-LYZ) To clean of living microorganisms.

strait Narrow passage of water connecting two oceans or lakes.

striated (STRY-AY-tuhd) Striped.

subatomic particles Particles making up an atom, including protons, electrons, and neutrons.

subduction zone Area where one plate of Earth's crust descends below another.

sublimation (SUH-bluh-MAY-shun) When a solid changes into a gas without passing through a liquid state first.

submersible (sub-MUHR-suh buhl) Vehicle designed to operate underwater.

superconductor Substance that has no electrical resistance at very low temperatures.

superheated Liquid heated above its boiling point without it turning into a vapor.

synthetic Humanmade; artificial.

taiga (TY-guh) Subarctic forest.

terrestrial planets The planets similar to Earth in composition: Mercury, Venus, Mars, and Earth.

tetrahedron (TEH-truh-HEE-druhn) Three-dimensional shape that has four faces.

thaw To melt.

three dimensional Having height, length, and depth.

time zone Region where the same standard time applies.

trace element Element found in tiny quantities, especially one that is essential for a living organism.

trade wind Wind that blows around Earth almost continuously in one direction.

transistor Device that controls the flow of electricity in electronic equipment.

tremor (TREH-muhr) Quiver or tremble in Earth's surface just before or after an earthquake.

trilobite (TRY-luh-BYT) Extinct, marine invertebrate that resembled a pill bug.

turbine (TUHR-buhn) Engine powered by a rotating blade.

twilight (TWY-lyt) Dusk and dawn.

urban From the city.

valence (VAY-luhnts) Measure of an element's ability to react with other elements.

velocity (vuh-LAH-suh-tee) How quickly an object moves in a certain direction.

void (VOYD) Empty space.

volatile (VAH-luh-tuhl) Readily vaporized (turned to gas).

voltage (VOHL-tij) Electrical potential energy that can be converted into another form.

waterspout Tornado over water that whips up spray.

white hot Incandescing (glowing) white at a high temperature.

windward Facing in the direction the prevailing wind travels.

Subject Indexes

CHEMISTRY

Acetic acid **1:**10; **2:**119–120
acids and bases **1:**10–11;
   5:355; **9:**676–677
acrylic fibers **10:**731
acrylic paints **8:**579
actinides **8:**595
actinium **8:**595
adenine **1:**71–72
adenosine triphosphate (ATP)
   1:71
aerogel **8:**633
Agent Orange **5:**336
air distillation **8:**573
albumen **9:**645
alchemists **2:**121, 122–123
aldehyde groups **2:**95
aldoses **2:**95
alizarin **3:**197
alkali metals **6:**468–469
alkaline earth metals **6:**469
alkaloids **1:**26–27
alkanes, isomers of **5:**382
alkenes **5:**352, 353
alkynes **5:**352, 353
alloys **1:**28–29; **6:**472; **8:**607
   aluminum **6:**429
   copper **3:**164, 165
   gold **4:**317
   hydrogen atoms in **3:**191
   made in space **9:**711
   magnesium **6:**428, 429
   magnetism **6:**435
   manganese **6:**437
   silver **9:**691
   See also brass; bronze; iron;
      steel
alnico **6:**435
alpha helix **9:**644
alpha particles **1:**57; **5:**385;
   7:526; **9:**654–655
aluminum **1:**30–31; **8:**564
   alloys **6:**429
aluminum bronze **1:**29; **3:**165
aluminum hydroxide **1:**31

aluminum oxide **1:**30, 31
aluminum silicate **1:**30
aluminum sulfate **1:**31
alums **1:**30
amalgamation, gold **4:**317
amalgams **1:**29
amine group **1:**68, 69
amino acids **1:**68, 69;
   8:567, 633; **9:**644, 645
ammonia **1:**10, 11; **5:**355;
   7:503, 531
   industrial production **2:**105;
      5:355; **7:**531
   reaction with hydrochloric
      acid **1:**11
ammonium chloride **1:**11
ammonium cyanate **1:**69
ammonium ions **1:**11; **5:**375;
   7:503
Anaximenes **2:**121–122
anesthetics **1:**26, 27
anions **5:**374; **9:**646
anthracene **3:**197
anthracite **2:**98, 140
antibodies **9:**645
antimony **6:**471
apeiron **2:**121
aqua regia **4:**316
argon **4:**295
aromatic compounds
   5:353, 382–383; **8:**601
arsenic **6:**471
arsenic oxide **6:**471
asphalt **8:**587
astatine **3:**235; **5:**335, 336;
   6:471
atomic mass **1:**56–57
atomic mass number
   and isotopes **5:**384
   See also atomic weight
atomic mass units
   and isotopes **5:**384
   See also atomic weight
atomic number **1:**56; **5:**384;
   8:584, 593; **9:**646
atomic weight **2:**125;
   8:591, 593

See also atomic mass number
atoms **1:55–57; 2:**122, 150;
   3:234–235; **6:**451; **8:**583
   electrons in **1:**56; **2:**107, 145;
      3:227–228, 234–235;
      5:396–397; **6:**418; **8:**583, 584
   nucleus See nucleus, atomic
   shells **1:**57; **3:**234–235;
      5:396–397; **8:**584
   structure See subatomic
      structure
ATP (adenosine triphosphate)
   1:71
Avogadro's hypothesis **8:**590–591
azo dyes **3:**197
azote **2:**124

Bakelite **8:**619
baking soda **6:**468–469
barium **6:**469
barium sulfate (barite)
   6:419, 469
base bullion **9:**693
bases **1:**10, 11
bases, DNA **1:**71–2
bases See acids and bases
bauxite **1:**30, 31
bends, the **6:**442
benzene **2:**139; **5:**353; **8:**601
   and isomers **5:**382–383
beryllium **6:**469
beryllium dichloride **7:**503
biochemistry **1:**68–73;
   2:123, 125
bioremediation **1:**70
blast furnace **2:**118; **5:**378,
   379; **6:**458, 473; **9:**692–693
bonds, chemical **7:**501–502
   covalent **2:**150, 151; **5:**375;
      7:500–501, 502, 503
   hydrogen **2:**92; **6:**414; **7:**503
   ionic **2:**150, 151
   in liquids **6:**414–415
   London forces **6:**415
   metallic **6:**468; **7:**501
   peptide **1:**68
   polar **6:**414

saturated and unsaturated
   6:412
bornite **9:**693
boron **6:**471
boron trichloride **7:**503
Boyle's law **4:**293
brass **1:**29; **3:**165; **6:**473
bromine **5:**335–336, 337
1-bromo-1-nitroethane **5:**382
1-bromo-2-nitroethane **5:**382
Bronsted–Lowry theory **1:**11
bronze **1:**28, 29; **3:**164, 165;
   6:472
   aluminum bronze **1:**29;
      3:165
   manganese bronze **6:**437
Bronze Age **6:**472
Brownian motion **6:**415
buckminsterfullerene **2:**98
burning (combustion) **8:**573
butane **5:**353, 382
butanol, reaction with acetic
   acid **2:**119–120
butene **5:**353
butyl acetate **2:**119–120

Calcium **1:**78; **6:**469; **8:**594
calcium bicarbonate **2:**101;
   5:331
calcium carbonate **1:**78
calcium fluoride (fluorite;
   fluorspar) **1:**78; **6:**411, 419
calcium hydrogen carbonate
   9:677
calcium hydroxide (slaked
   lime) **1:**78; **6:**469
calcium hydroxyphosphate
   1:78
calcium magnesium carbonate
   6:469
calcium oxide (lime; quicklime)
   1:78; **6:**411
calcium sulfate, hydrated **1:**78;
   6:469
calomel **6:**459
carbohydrates **2:**94–96
carbolic acid **8:**601
carbon **2:**97–99; **7:**532
   cycle **1:**54
   isotopes **2:**97, 108; **5:**384,
      385; **9:**654, 655, 656–657
   and organic compounds

Volume numbers appear in **boldface type** followed by colons. Page numbers in **boldface type** refer to main articles and their illustrations. Page numbers in *italic type* refer to additional illustrations.

8:566–567
structure and bonding **2**:*98*
carbon dating
See radiocarbon dating
carbon dioxide **2**:97, 99, **100–101**
atmospheric **1**:52, *54*; **2**:100
density **3**:183
solid (dry ice) **2**:100; **3**:195;
8:606; **9**:*701*
to make sodas **8**:607
carbon disulfide **2**:99
carbonic acid **2**:99, 100
carbon monoxide **2**:97, 99,
139; **8**:573
carbonyl groups, in sugars **2**:95
carboxylic acid group **1**:68;
5:355
carotene **5**:352
catalysts **2**:**104–105**, 120; **6**:470
catalytic converters **2**:*105*;
4:*313*
cations **5**:374; **9**:646
caustic soda **3**:216
Celanese **10**:731
celluloid **8**:619
cellulose **2**:94; **10**:731
cellulose acetate **10**:731
cellulose lacquer paints **8**:579
cell walls, phospholipids **6**:413
cement **6**:469
cesium **6**:468; **9**:715
cetyl palmitate **6**:413
CFCs *See* chlorofluorocarbons
chain reactions **6**:407
chalcopyrite **6**:472; **9**:693
charcoal **2**:97
Charles's law **4**:293
chemical reactions **2**:104,
116–120; **6**:451
activation energy **2**:104, 105
displacement reactions **8**:571
equations **2**:117, 124–125
luminescent **6**:419
oxidation **8**:**570–571**, 572
produced by light **6**:407
reversible **2**:118
speed **2**:117
See also catalysts
chemistry **2**:**121–125**
organic **2**:125, 139; **8**:**566–567**
physical **2**:125; **8**:**608–609**
chirality **5**:383
chlorides **9**:677
chlorine **2**:150; **5**:335, 337
bonding **7**:502
as a free radical **5**:375
poisons **5**:336
reaction with sodium

2:118–19; **5**:374–5; **8**:571
relative atomic mass **5**:384
chlorofluorocarbons (CFCs)
1:33; **5**:337
environmental effects **1**:53,
75; **4**:314; **5**:337; **8**:*574*,
575, 601, 631
chlorophyll **2**:94, 101; **6**:429;
8:571
cholesteric liquid crystals
6:417
cholesteryl benzoate **6**:416
chromatography **2**:93
chromium, in steel alloys **5**:379
cinnabar **6**:459
cis- isomers **5**:383
citric acid **1**:10, *71*
coal **2**:98
coal gas **2**:139; **8**:601
coal tar **2**:139
cobalt **5**:378, 385; **9**:655
magnetism **6**:**434–435**
cocaine **1**:26, 27
cochineal **3**:196
coconut oil **6**:*412*
codeine **1**:26
codons **1**:73
coke **2**:98, 138–139
collagen **9**:645
collodion **8**:604
combustion (burning) **8**:573
combustion analysis **8**:567
compounds **2**:**150–151**
condensation reactions **1**:68–69
converters, catalytic **2**:*105*;
4:*313*
copper **3**:**164–165**; **6**:*468*; **7**:491
blister **9**:693
compounds **3**:164–165; **8**:*594*
electrical conductance **3**:*164,
165*, 215
extraction **2**:121; **6**:472;
9:693
purification **3**:217
copper chloride **3**:165
copper (I) oxide (cuprous
oxide) **3**:164; **7**:*501*
copper (II) oxide (cupric oxide)
3:165
copper (II) sulfate (cupric
sulfate) **3**:165
Courtelle **10**:731
cracking processes **8**:601
cryolite **1**:30
crystals **3**:**176–177**; **9**:700–701
grown in space **9**:711
ice **5**:361
liquid crystals **6**:**416–417**

cupellation **6**:473
cuprammonium ion **3**:165
curare **1**:26
curarine **1**:26
curine **1**:26
curium **8**:595
cyclohexane **5**:*353*
cyclonite (RDX) **4**:263
cyclopropane **2**:*99*
cytosine **1**:71–72

Dacron **10**:731
DDT **5**:336
decompression sickness **6**:442
De Materia Medica **1**:27
deoxyribonucleic acid
See DNA
desalination **8**:569
detergents **3**:**186–187**; **10**:730
See also soaps
deuterium **5**:354
and fusion **4**:288–289
dialysis **10**:757
diamond **2**:97–*98*, *99*; **3**:177;
4:300, 301
diborane **6**:471
1,2-dibromoethene **5**:383
dimers **8**:633
dimethyl ether **5**:382
2,2-dimethylpropane **5**:382
dinitrobenzene, isomers **5**:383
dioxins **1**:70; **5**:336; **8**:601
dipoles, molecular **8**:627
disaccharides **2**:95–96
displacement reactions **8**:571
distillation **2**:120, 122; **8**:607
air **8**:573
of coal tar **2**:139
destructive **2**:138–139
fractional **7**:499; **8**:573
for refining **9**:665
DNA (deoxyribonucleic acid)
1:71–72; **4**:283; **6**:417;
10:767
and protein formation **1**:73;
9:645
structure **1**:*69*, 72–73; **7**:502
dolomite **6**:469
drugs (medicinal)
alkaloid **1**:26, 27
isomers **5**:383
magnesium medicinal
compounds **6**:429
ocean sources **6**:444

dry ice **2**:100; **3**:195; **8**:606;
9:*701*
dyes **3**:**196–197**; **8**:621
See also paints; pigments
dynamite **7**:493

Einsteinium **8**:595
electrolysis **1**:78; **3**:**216–217**;
4:317; **9**:665
for metal extraction **6**:473
to produce magnesium **6**:428
electrolytes **3**:216
electrons **3**:**225–228**
in atoms **1**:*56*; **2**:107, 145;
3:227 228, 234–235;
5:396–397; **6**:418; **8**:583
charge **3**:227
and luminescence **6**:418
mass **1**:*56*
electroplating **3**:*216*, 217;
9:691
elements **2**:124, 150;
3:**234–235**; **8**:583
of the Greek philosophers
2:122; **4**:275
half-life **4**:307; **9**:656
oxidation numbers **8**:570–571
table of *See* periodic table
See also isotopes
emulsions **7**:498–499
enantiomers **5**:383
endorphins **1**:27
energy, activation **2**:104, 105
enzymes **1**:71; **2**:104, 105, 120;
9:645
are proteins **2**:123
in detergent products **3**:187
proteolytic **3**:187
Epsom salts **6**:429
ergonovine **1**:26
esters **6**:412
ethane **2**:99; **5**:352, *353*
ethanol **5**:382
ethene **5**:352, *353*

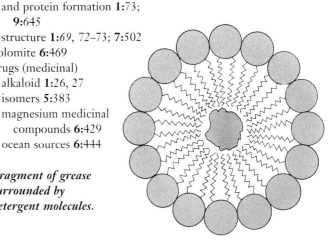

*Fragment of grease
surrounded by
detergent molecules.*

ethers **8**:567
ethylbutene **5**:353
ethylenediamine tetra-acetate (EDTA) **2**:151
ethyne **5**:352
explosives **4:262–263**
  for mining **7**:492–493

Fats and oils **6**:412, 413; **7**:499
  saturated and unsaturated **6**:*412*–413
fatty acids **6**:412
fermentation **2**:105, 123
ferric oxide (rust) **5**:379; **8**:*570*
fiberglass **8**:621
fibers, synthetic **10:731**
fillings, tooth **1**:*29*
filtration **7**:499
fireflies **6**:419
fireworks **4**:262
flotation **6**:473; **8**:565; **9**:692
fluorescence **3**:197, 219; **6**:418, 419
fluorine **5**:335, 336, 337
fluorite *See* calcium fluoride
foods, genetically modified (GM) **1**:73
forensic science **6**:419; **9**:705; **10**:767
formic acid **1**:10
formulas, chemical **2**:117
francium **6**:468
free radicals **5**:375; **6**:412
fructose **2**:95, *96*
fuel, hydrogen as a **5**:355
fuel cells **5**:355
fullerene **2**:98
functional groups **8**:567

Gallium **8**:594
galvanized iron **5**:379
gases **4:292–295**; **6**:*451*; **9**:700
  gas laws **4**:292, 293, 294; **8**:608–609, 637
  mixtures **7**:498, *499*
  noble/inert **4**:*295*; **5**:342; **7**:500, 502, 532
gasoline **2**:105; **3**:183; **8**:600–601
genes **1**:73; **9**:645
genetic engineering **1**:70, 73
genetics **1**:71–72
gentian violet **3**:197
geochemistry **4**:307
germanium **6**:471; **8**:594
glass **7**:501
glowworms **6**:419
glucose **2**:*94*, 95, *96*, 151
glycerol **6**:412

glycogen **2**:96
gold **2**:122; **4:316–317**; **6**:470
  mining or panning for **4**:317; **6**:473; **7**:493, *494*
  "yellow" **9**:691
graphite **2**:97, *98*; **7**:*532*; **9**:701
grease **3**:*186*
  and soap **6**:413
Greeks, ancient **2**:121–122; **3**:233
  and matter **6**:451
guanine **1**:71–72
gunpowder **4**:*262*, 263; **7**:492–493
gypsum **1**:78; **6**:469

Haber process **2**:105; **5**:355; **7**:531
half-life **4**:307; **9**:656
halogens **5:335–337**
helium **1**:57; **3**:183; **4**:295; **5**:342; **8**:*583*
  and fusion **4**:*288–289*; **6**:450
hematite **5**:379
hemocyanin **3**:165
hemoglobin **1**:69; **9**:645
henna **3**:196
heroin **1**:27
hexacyanoferrate (III) **5**:375
hexamine chromium (II) **5**:375
hexane, immiscible with water **6**:415
hormones **9**:645
hydrocarbons **2**:139; **5**:*352–353*, 353; **8**:567
  See also natural gas; organic chemistry
hydrochloric acid **1**:10–11; **2**:119
hydrocyanic acid **5**:355
hydrogen **3**:235; **5:354–355**
  in airships **3**:183; **5**:*354*
  discovery **1**:10; **2**:123
  and fusion **4**:288–289; **6**:450
  ions **1**:10–11
  isotopes **4**:288–289; **5**:354
  liquid **3**:174; **5**:355
  nonpolar **8**:*627*
  in the Universe **7**:532
hydrogenation, of fats **6**:412
hydrogen bonding **2**:92; **6**:414; **7**:*503*; **10**:730
hydrogen chloride **7**:502; **8**:*627*

hydrogen iodide **2**:118
hydrogen peroxide **5**:355
hydrogen sulfide **5**:355
hydronium ions **1**:11
hydroxides **8**:572

Ideal gas law **4**:293, 294; **8**:609, 637
illite **2**:*127*
indicators **1**:11
interstitial solid solutions **1**:28–29
iodine **2**:118; **5**:*335*, 336, 337; **9**:701
ion exchange **5**:374
ions **2**:150–151; **5:374–375**; **7**:501; **9**:677
  polyatomic **2**:151
iron and steel **5:378–379**
  alloy steels **5**:379
  carbon steel **1**:29; **5**:379
  cast iron **5**:379
  Hadfield steel **6**:437
  iron abundance **8**:564
  iron extraction **5**:*379*; **6**:472; **9**:692–693
  iron ore in Australia **1**:61
  magnetism **5**:378–379; **6**:434–436
  pig iron **5**:379; **9**:693
  reactivity of iron **6**:470
  stainless steel **1**:28, 29; **5**:379
  steel **1**:28, 29; **8**:607; **9**:665
  steel manufacture **5**:379; **6**:472–473
  wrought iron **5**:379
  See also rust
isomers **5**:353, **382–383**
isotopes **3**:235; **5:384–385**; **7**:526, 539; **8**:593; **9**:654
  carbon **2**:97, 108; **5**:384, 385; **9**:654, 655, *656–657*
  cosmogenic **9**:*656–657*
  hydrogen **4**:288–9; **5**:354
  plutonium **8**:626
  and positron emission **3**:226; **5**:385; **9**:655
  tellurium **6**:*471*
  uranium **3**:235; **4**:295; **5**:384–385; **7**:526; **9**:656

Kaolinite **2**:*127*
karats **4**:317

keratin **9**:644
ketones **2**:95
kinetics **8**:609
Krebs cycle *See* citric acid
krypton **4**:*295*

Lactic acid, isomers **5**:*382*, *383*
lanthanides **8**:595
latex paints **8**:579
lattices, crystal **9**:701
lawrencium **8**:595
leaching **6**:473
lead **9**:665, 693
  extraction from ores **6**:473
lead azide **4**:262
lead iodide **2**:119
lead nitrate, reaction with potassium iodide **2**:119
lidocaine **1**:26
life, simulating early conditions for **1**:72
ligands **5**:375
light
  and chemical reactions **6**:407
  rotation by sugars **2**:96
lime *See* calcium oxide
limestone **6**:469
  uses **6**:411
linseed oil **6**:412–413; **8**:578
lipase **3**:187
lipids **6:412–413**
liquid crystals **6:416–417**
liquids **6:414–415**, *451*; **9**:700
lithium **1**:57; **6**:468
lithium carbonate **6**:469
litmus **1**:11
London forces **6**:415
luminescence **6:418–419**, 469
luminol **6**:419
Lycra **10**:731

Macromolecules **5**:374; **7**:*501*
magenta dye **3**:197
magnesia (magnesium oxide) **6**:428
magnesium **6:428–429**, 469
  ores **6**:429
  reaction with sulfuric acid **9**:677
magnesium carbonate **6**:429
magnesium oxide **6**:429
magnesium sulfate **6**:429
magnetite **5**:379
malachite **2**:121
manganate ion **6**:437
manganese **6**:437; **8**:594
  ores **6**:437

Volume numbers appear in **boldface type** followed by colons. Page numbers in **boldface type** refer to main articles and their illustrations. Page numbers in *italic type* refer to additional illustrations.

oxidation states **6:**437; **8:**571
manganese bronze **6:**437
manganese dioxide **6:**437;
    8:571
manganese (II) oxide **6:**437
manganese (IV) oxide **6:**437,
    470
manganese (II) sulfate **6:**437,
    470
mannose **2:**95
mass spectrometers **8:**567;
    9:657
matte **9:**693
matter **6:**451
    ancient Greeks and **2:**121–122;
        6:451
    See also atoms; gases; liquids;
        solids
mauve dye **3:**197
medicines *See* drugs
    (medicinal)
mendelevium **8:**592, 595
mercuric nitrate **6:**459
mercurous chloride **6:**458
mercury (metal) **1:**24;
    6:458–459, 473
    amalgams **1:**29; **6:**459
    in barometers **6:**458
    poisoning **6:**459
    to purify gold **4:**317; **6:**473
mesomorphic state **6:**416
metalloids **6:**471
metallurgy **6:**472–473
metals **6:**468–470
    alkali **6:**468–469
    alkaline earth **6:**469
    atoms **3:**177; **6:**468; **7:**501
    bonds **6:**468; **7:**501
    crystal structure **3:**177
    extraction from ores **6:**473;
        8:565
    mixtures *See* alloys
    post-transition **6:**470
    reaction with acids **9:**677
    reactivity series **6:**470
    scrap **8:**565; **9:**665
    sheet **6:***469*
    transition **6:**470; **8:**594
    See also metallurgy
methane **2:***99*; **5:**352, 354–355;
    7:*503*
    burning **8:**573
    in natural gas **7:**522
2-methylbutane **5:**382
methylpentene **5:**353
methylpropane **5:**382
micelles **3:***186*
milk of magnesia **6:**429

mixtures **7:498–499**
    of liquids **6:**415; **7:498–499**
mole **1:**11
molecules **5:**374; **7:500–503**
    polar and nonpolar **7:**500–501;
        8:*627*
    See also isomers
molybdenum **8:**594
monoglycerides **6:**413
monomers **7:**501; **8:**633
monosaccharides **2:**95
montmorillonite **2:***127*
mordants **3:**197
morphine **1:***26*, 27

Naphthalene **2:**139
natural gas **2:**98; **5:**342; **7:**522;
    8:600
nematic crystals **6:**417
neon **4:***295*
neutralization reactions **1:**10
neutrons **1:**57; **3:**234, 235;
    7:526, 539
    discovery **7:**526, 539; **8:**584;
        10:726
nickel **3:**165; **5:**378, 379
nitrates **5:**375; **9:**677
nitric acid **2:***104*; **7:**531
nitrides **7:**531
nitrogen **1:**52; **2:**124; **7:530–531**
    and decompression sickness
        6:441–442
    liquid **3:**174, 175; **7:***530*
nitroglycerin **4:***262–263*
nitrous oxide, a greenhouse
    gas **4:***313*
noble gases *See* gases,
    noble/inert
nonmetals **7:532**
Novocaine **1:**26
nucleases, restrictive **1:**73
nucleus, atomic **1:***56*; **3:**234,
    235; **7:***526*
    forces in **4:**276–277; **8:**585;
        10:726–727
    See also neutrons; protons
nylon **1:**69; **8:**619–620, *632*,
    633; **10:**731

Oil, crude (petroleum) **2:**98;
    7:530–531; **8:**600
    refining **2:**116; **8:**601
oils *See* fats and oils
olefins **8:**601
opiates **1:**27
opium **1:**27
ores
    dressing **9:**692

metal extraction from **6:**473;
    8:565; **9:**692–693
organic chemistry **2:**125, 139;
    8:566–567
    See also alkaloids;
        carbohydrates;
        hydrocarbons; lipids;
        plastics; proteins
organochlorines **5:**336
Orlon **10:**731
Ostwald ammonia oxidation
    process **7:**531
oxidation **8:570–571**, 572, 573
oxidation numbers **8:**570–571
oxides **8:**571, 572
oxygen **7:**532; **8:572–573**
    atmospheric **1:**52, 54; **8:**572,
        581
    cycle **8:***572*
    discovery **2:**123; **8:***573*
ozone **1:**53; **6:**407; **8:**572

Paints **8:578–579**
    luminous **6:**469
    manufacture **6:**413
    See also dyes
pastes **7:**499
patina **3:**165
PCBs (polychlorinated
    biphenyls) **1:**70; **8:587**
pentaerythritol tetranitrate
    (PETN) **4:**263
pentane **5:**382
pepsin **2:**105
peptide bonds **1:**68; **9:**644
periodic table **1:**56, 57; **2:**125;
    3:234; **8:590–595**, 626
    See also elements
pesticides **1:**70
petrochemicals **8:600–601**,
    632–633
petroleum *See* oil, crude
petroleum ether **7:**499
pH **1:**11

phenol **8:**601
phenolphthalein **1:**11
phlogiston **2:**124; **8:**573
phospholipids **6:**413
phosphorescence **6:**418–419
phosphorus **6:**419
phosphorus pentachloride
    7:*503*
photons, and chemical
    reactions **6:**407
photosynthesis **2:**94; **8:**570,
    571
    and carbon dioxide **1:**54;
        2:101
    and oxygen **8:**572
phthalic acid **6:**413
phthalocyanines **3:**197; **6:**437
physical chemistry **2:**125;
    8:608–609
pigments **3:**196; **8:***578, 579*,
    621
    See also dyes
plaster of Paris **1:**78
plasticizers **8:**579, 621
plastics **7:**501; **8:618–621**
platinum, catalysts of **2:**105
plutonium **4:**271; **8:***595*, **626**
poisons **1:**26; **5:**336
    mercury **6:**459
polar forces **6:**414
polarity **7:**500–501; **8:627**
polonium **9:**655
polyamides **8:**633
polychlorinated biphenyls
    See PCBs
polyesters **8:**620; **10:**731
polycthylene (polythene)
    5:352, 353; **8:**620, 632
polymers **6:**407; **7:**501;
    8:632–633; **10:**731
    plastics **8:**619
    polymerization **5:**353; **8:**633
    See also proteins

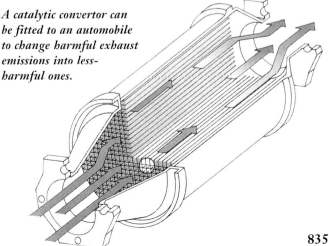

*A catalytic convertor can
be fitted to an automobile
to change harmful exhaust
emissions into less-
harmful ones.*

polypeptides **9**:644, *645*
polyphosphazene **8**:633
polysaccharides **2**:96; **7**:501
polystyrene **8**:633
polyurethanes **8**:579; **10**:731
post-transition metals **6**:470
potassium **6**:468, 470; **8**:594, *608*; **9**:714–715
potassium fluoride **5**:337
potassium iodide **2**:119
potassium nitrate **6**:469
potassium permanganate **6**:437
procaine **1**:26, 27
Prontosil **3**:197
protactinium **8**:595
proteins **1**:68–69; **7**:501, 502; **9**:644–645
  formation **1**:73; **8**:633
  See also enzymes
protium **5**:354
protons **1**:57; **3**:234, 235; **7**:538, 539; **9**:646
PTFE (polytetrafluoroethene) **5**:337; **8**:620
puddling furnace **5**:379
PVC **8**:621

Quicklime (calcium oxide) **1**:78; **6**:411
quicksilver **6**:458

Radiocarbon dating **2**:108, 133; **5**:385; **8**:612; **9**:656–657
radioisotopes **5**:385
radium **6**:469; **9**:655
radon **4**:295
rare earth metals **8**:595
reactions, chemical *See* chemical reactions
reactivity series **6**:470
recycling, chemical **2**:120
redox reactions **8**:570, 571
reducing agents **8**:570
refining **6**:473; **7**:551; **9**:665
relative atomic mass **5**:384
resins
  alkyd **6**:413
  epoxy **1**:29; **8**:620
  in paints **8**:579
respiration **2**:101; **8**:571
reverberatory furnace **9**:693
ribonucleic acid *See* RNA
RNA (ribonucleic acid) **1**:73; **9**:645
rock phosphate **1**:78
rubidium **6**:468; **9**:715
rust **2**:122; **5**:379; **8**:*570*, 571

Saccharides **2**:95–96
salts **1**:10; **9**:676–677
salt *See* sodium chloride
sand **6**:471
scandium **8**:594
scientific method **8**:613
seawater
  drinking water from **8**:569
  magnesium from **6**:428–429
  table salt from **6**:428–429
selenium **6**:471
Semtex **4**:263
sheet silicate **2**:127
silica (silicon dioxide) **2**:126; **9**:679
  tiles **1**:17
silicon **6**:471; **9**:679
silicon carbide **2**:99; **9**:679
silicones **8**:579, 620, 633
silver **3**:183, *217*; **9**:690–691, 693
silver azide **9**:691
silver bromide **5**:*337*; **9**:691
silver chloride **9**:691
silver cyanide **9**:691
silver iodide **3**:195; **9**:691
silver nitrate **9**:691
silver oxide **9**:691
silver sulfide **9**:691
sintering **3**:191; **9**:693
slag **5**:379
slaked lime (calcium hydroxide) **1**:78; **6**:469
smelting **6**:473; **8**:565; **9**:692–693
soaps **3**:186; **6**:*412*, 413
  See also detergents
sodium **2**:150; **6**:468
  reaction with chlorine **2**:118–119; **5**:374–375; **8**:571
sodium azide **4**:263
sodium bicarbonate **6**:468–469
sodium carbonate
  hydrated **6**:468
  reaction with acetic acid **1**:*10*
  reaction with hydrochloric acid **2**:119
sodium chloride (salt) **2**:119, 150–*151*; **3**:177; **8**:571; **9**:676
  crystals **9**:*677*, *700*
  dissolving in water **8**:607, 627
  electrolysis **3**:216–217

ionic lattice **2**:*151*; **5**:*375*
  from seawater **7**:493
sodium hydroxide **3**:216; **6**:468
  reaction with sulfuric acid **1**:10; **2**:117, 118
sodium nitrate **4**:263
sodium sulfate **2**:117, 151
solders **1**:29
solids **6**:*451*; **9**:700–701
  ionic **5**:374
solutions **6**:415; **7**:*498*; **8**:607
  solid **8**:607
solvent extraction **7**:499
soot **8**:573
spandex fibers **10**:731
spectrographs **9**:715
spectrometers **9**:*714*, 715
  mass **8**:567; **9**:657
spinnerets **10**:731
starches **2**:94, 96; **8**:633
statistical mechanics **8**:609
steam reforming **5**:355
steel *See* iron and steel
stereoisomerism **5**:383
strong nuclear force **3**:235; **4**:276–277
  carrier particles for **8**:585
strontium **6**:469
styrene **8**:601
styrofoam **8**:632
subatomic structure **1**:56–57; **7**:539; **10**:725–727
sublimation **2**:100; **5**:361; **8**:606; **9**:*701*
sucrose **2**:*96*
sugar(s) **2**:94–96; **3**:*191*; **9**:700
sulfates **5**:375; **9**:677
sulfur, removal from fuels **8**:601
sulfur bacteria **8**:577
sulfur hexafluoride **7**:*503*
sulfuric acid **8**:572
  reaction with sodium hydroxide **1**:10; **2**:117, 118
sulfur trioxide **8**:572
surface tension **2**:92–93; **10**:730
  and surfactants **3**:186
surfactants **3**:186
symbols, chemical **2**:117
synthetic fibers **10**:731

Tartrazine **3**:197
TCDD (dioxin in Agent

Orange **5**:336
technetium **3**:235
Teflon **5**:337; **8**:*619*, 620
tellurium **6**:*471*; **8**:593
Terylene **10**:731
tetrachloromethane **6**:415
thermoplastics **8**:620
thermosets **8**:620
thorium **8**:595, 638
thymine **1**:71–72
tin **5**:379; **9**:665
titanium **8**:594
toluene **2**:139; **8**:601
trans-isomers **5**:383
transition metals **6**:470; **8**:594
transuranic elements **3**:235; **8**:626
trichloromethane **6**:414
triglycerides **6**:412
trinitrotoluene (TNT) **4**:263
tritium **5**:354
turpentine **8**:578

Ultracentrifuges **1**:69
uranium **8**:595
  enriched **4**:295; **5**:384–385
  isotopes **3**:235; **4**:295; **5**:384–385; **7**:526; **9**:656
uranium hexafluoride **4**:295; **5**:337, 384–385
urea **1**:69
urease **1**:71

Valence **8**:591–592
  valence shells **7**:501–503; **8**:592
vanadium **8**:594
van der Waals forces **7**:502
vinblastine **1**:26
vincristine **1**:26
viscose **10**:*731*
vitamins, and free radicals **5**:375

Water **10**:784–785
  formation **8**:571
  hard **3**:186; **5**:374; **9**:677
  molecules **2**:92; **7**:503
  pH **1**:11
  a solvent **6**:415
  states **6**:457; **8**:*606*, *607*
  surface tension **10**:730
waxes **6**:413
weak nuclear force **4**:277
  carrier particles for **8**:585

Xenon **4**:295
X rays

Volume numbers appear in **boldface type** followed by colons. Page numbers in **boldface type** refer to main articles and their illustrations. Page numbers in *italic type* refer to additional illustrations.

and barium sulfate **6**:469
X-ray diffraction **1**:72; **10**:798

Yttrium **8**:594

Zeolites **3**:191; **5**:374
zinc **5**:379; **8**:571

EARTH

Abrasion **5**:363
air, density **1**:25
air currents *See* jet streams
air (atmospheric) pressure **1**:23–25, 52–53; **7**:485
and monsoons **7**:506
albedo **2**:130
alluvial fans **4**:253; **9**:671
Alps **10**:775
altitude **1**:*24*, 52–53; **2**:*131*; **4**:278
alumina **1**:30
aluminum **8**:564
Alvin (submersible) **5**:359
amazon stone **7**:*490*
amber **4**:285, 300
amethysts **4**:300, 301; **9**:650
ammonites **3**:172, 173; **4**:*284*, *285*; **5**:391; **6**:467; **10**:759
amphibians **3**:189; **7**:497; **8**:581, 589, 599
amphiboles **9**:673
andesite magma **6**:426, 427; **8**:623
anemometers **10**:796
ANGUS (underwater camera sled) **5**:359
anhydrite **8**:598–599
ankylosaurs **3**:173
Antarctic Circumpolar Current **1**:50; **8**:577
Antarctic Treaty **8**:629
anthracite **2**:98, 140
anticlines **7**:515, *522*
anticyclones **10**:790
aquifers **5**:*330*, 331–332, 333, 357; **10**:785
archaeobacteria **5**:359
Archaeopteryx **4**:*264*
Archean eon **8**:634
arches, sea **4**:254

Arctic region **7**:535; **8**:628, 629; **10**:762
argenite **9**:690
arroyos **9**:670; **10**:775
Atacama Trench **9**:707
atmosphere **1**:51–54; **2**:134; **3**:199, 220
and auroras **1**:59
gases **1**:52, 59; **2**:100; **7**:530
humidity **5**:348–349
layers **1**:*52*–54; **5**:386
past composition **1**:54; **4**:315
See also clouds; ozone layer; stratosphere; winds
atmospheric pressure *See* air (atmospheric) pressure
atolls **5**:*380*, 381
auroras **1**:54, **58**–**59**; **6**:431, 435; **8**:617
australopithecines **4**:283–284
avalanches **1**:**62**–**63**
Axial Volcano **3**:171

Badlands **4**:255
Baikal, Lake **5**:393
balloons, weather **7**:*484*; **10**:796
barite **6**:419
See barium sulfate
barium sulfate (barite) **6**:419; **8**:564
barographs **1**:*23*, 24
barometers **1**:24, 25; **6**:458; **7**:485
bars, in rivers **9**:671, 679
basalt **5**:366, 367; **6**:426–427; **7**:490; **9**:672
island **5**:380, 381
batholiths **5**:367; **6**:427
bauxite **1**:30, 31
beaches, sandy **9**:679; **10**:787
Beaufort scale **10**:796
belemnites **3**:172, 173; **5**:391
berms **2**:143
biogenic rocks **9**:687
biomes **1**:74
biosphere **1**:**74**–**75**
black smokers **5**:359
bogs **10**:793
boreholes **5**:357
bottom water **1**:50
Brazil Current **1**:50
breakwaters **2**:143
breccias **9**:687
Burgess Shale **2**:89

Cabochons **4**:301
cairngorm **9**:650

calcite **6**:410; **7**:491; **9**:673
calcium **1**:78
calcium carbonate, in limestone **6**:410, 411
calcium fluoride (fluorite; fluorspar) **1**:78; **6**:411, 419
calcium hydroxide (slaked lime) **1**:78; **6**:469
calcium oxide (lime; quicklime) **1**:78; **6**:411, 469
calderas **3**:170, 171
Cambrian period **2**:**88**–**89**; **4**:305, 306; **8**:580
North America during **2**:*89*; **8**:581
Canadian Shield **7**:533, 535
canyons **2**:**90**–**91**; **5**:*394*; **10**:774
submarine **2**:90, 91, 158; **6**:444
carbon cycle **1**:54
carbon dating *See* radiocarbon dating
carbon dioxide
atmospheric **1**:52, *54*; **2**:100
and global warming **2**:101, 140; **4**:279, *313*–314
and stalactites/stalagmites **2**:101
Carboniferous period **2**:138; **5**:364; **7**:496; **8**:580, 588
See also Mississippian period; Pennsylvanian period
Carlsbad Caverns **2**:110; **5**:*331*
cartographers **6**:438, 439
caves **2**:**108**–**111**
limestone **2**:108, *109*–110; **5**:331; **6**:411
sea **2**:111; **4**:254
Cenozoic era **2**:**112**–**113**; **4**:305
periods *See* Quaternary period; Tertiary period
cephalopods **5**:391
cerargyrite **9**:690
ceratopsians **3**:173
Chagos Laccadive Plateau **5**:369
chalcopyrite **6**:472; **9**:693
chalk **1**:78; **3**:172, 173; **6**:410; **9**:687
Challenger Deep **6**:444

Challenger, HMS **6**:443; **7**:547
Channeled Scablands **2**:113; **5**:363
charcoal **2**:*97*
charts, nautical **6**:439
China, mapmaking **6**:439
Chinooks **10**:797
chondrites **6**:478
cinder cones **10**:*781*
cirques/corries **2**:129; **4**:254, 311–312; **5**:392, 395
clay **2**:**126**–**127**
cleavage **4**:301; **7**:491
cliffs **2**:111, **128**–**129**, 142
climate **2**:**130**–**133**
and erosion **4**:252
fluctuations **4**:315
and forests **4**:280
and grasslands **5**:324–325
and the Gulf Stream **5**:334
Paleozoic **8**:581
past **4**:315; **5**:362–365
and water **5**:357
See also deserts; global warming; ice ages; weather; winds
clouds **2**:**134**–**137**; **7**:486; **9**:662–663; **10**:*724*, 790
cumulonimbus (thunderclouds) **2**:*135*, 137; **6**:408–*409*
and meteorology **7**:485
seeding **3**:195; **9**:691
coal **2**:**138**–**140**; **4**:283
formation **1**:54; **2**:*139*, 140; **8**:589; **9**:687
mining **2**:139–140; **7**:*492*, 493

Isaac Newton observed how Earth's gravity causes an apple to fall to the ground from a tree.

coal gas **2**:139
coal tar **2**:139
coasts **2:141–143**; **5**:395; **7**:541
  beaches **9**:679; **10**:787
  floods **4**:273
coccoliths **9**:687
coesite **6**:475
Columbia River **3**:*199*
conglomerates **9**:687
continental climate **2**:132
continental drift **2:156–157**;
    3:202; **8**:582, 622–623
continental margins **7**:540
continental rise **7**:540
continental shelves **1**:49;
    2:158; **7**:540
continents **2:156–157**
  edges *See* continental shelves
  supercontinents *See*
      Gondwana; Laurasia;
      Pangaea
contour lines **6**:440
contrails **2**:137
convection currents, in the
    Earth's mantle **3**:202, *203*,
    204
copper **7**:491
coral reefs **2**:143; **5**:*395*; **8**:581
  Caribbean **2**:103
  Devonian period **3**:189
corals **7**:558
core, Earth's **3**:199, *201*, 202–203
Coriolis effect **1**:25; **5**:350;
    10:790, 795
corries *See* cirques/corries
craters **3:170–171**
  impact **3**:170–171; **6**:476–477
  lunar **3**:171, 198; **7**:509, 510
Cretaceous period **3:172–173**;
    6:467
  extinctions **3**:171, 173; **4**:265
  meteorite impact **3**:171, 173;
    4:265; **6**:467, 476
crevasses, glacial **4**:312
crinoids **7**:496
crust, Earth's **3**:199–200, *201*
cryolite **1**:30
crystals **3:176–177**; **4**:301
  See also gemstones
crystal systems **7**:491
currents, ocean *See* ocean
    currents
cyclones **4**:273; **5**:350; **10**:*790*
  See also hurricanes

Dams **4**:272–273; **5**:393
dating
  radiocarbon *See* radiocarbon

dating
  rocks **4**:304–305, 307; **6**:431;
    8:634; **9**:656
Deccan plateau **10**:741
deltas **2**:143; **3:180–181**;
    4:253; **9**:671; **10**:793
deposition **2**:142–143; **4**:253
deserts **1**:74; **2**:132;
    3:184–185, 194, *195*;
    5:*333*
  erosion **3**:185; **4**:254–255
  sand dunes **3**:185; **9**:679
detrital rocks **9**:687
Devonian period **3:188–189**;
    8:*580*
dew point **2**:134; **5**:349
diamond **2**:97–98, *99*; **3**:177;
    4:300, 301; **7**:491
dinosaurs **3**:173; **5**:*390, 391*
  extinction **1**:43; **2**:149;
    3:171, 173; **4**:265; **6**:476
  fossils **4**:283, 285
  Jurassic **6**:467
  Mesozoic **6**:*466*
diving bells **5**:369
diving suits **7**:547
dolerite **5**:367
dolomite **6**:411, 429, 469
dolostone **6**:411
downdrafts **10**:795
downwellings **7**:541, *543*
drainage basins **5**:395
drought **3:194–195**, 237; **4**:280
drumlins **2**:113; **4**:312
dry washes *See* wadis
dunes **2**:143; **3**:185; **9**:679
dust bowl **3**:195
dustdevils **10**:754
dust storms **4**:255
dykes **5**:367; **6**:427, 474–475

Earth **3:198–203**
  age **4**:305, 307
  circumference **4**:302
  flat or round? **3**:200
  gravity **1**:23; **3**:199; **4**:275;
    5:*328*
  infrared images of **5**:*370*
  magnetism **6**:*430*–431, 435;
    9:657
  seasons **9**:684–685
  structure **3**:199–200, *201*,
    202–203

surface without oceans **4**:*303*
  tilt **2**:130; **3**:203; **4**:250
  See also atmosphere
earthflows **4**:255
earthquakes **3:204–207**; **4**:257,
    266, 267
  in North America **3**:204–205,
    207; **4**:267; **7**:534
  and tidal waves **3**:205;
    10:744
easterlies **10**:788, 797
East Pacific Rise **5**:359
electron microprobes **7**:491
elements, native **7**:491
El Niño and La Niña **3:236–238**;
    7:547; **8**:*576, 577*
emeralds **4**:300, 301
ENSO **3**:236–237
Eocene epoch **2**:112; **10**:740,
    741
eons, geologic **4**:*304*; **8**:634
epochs, geologic **4**:*304*
equator **3**:199
equatorial currents **1**:49
eras, geologic **6**:466; **4**:*304*
erosion **4:252–525**; **9**:687
  by flowing water **4**:252–*253*;
    9:671; **10**:785
  by glaciers **4**:253–254, 311,
    312; **5**:395
  cliff **2**:128–*129*
  coastal **2**:142; **7**:541
  and deforestation **4**:279
  in deserts **3**:185; **4**:254–255
  forming clay **2**:127
  and landforms **5**:395
  mass wasting **4**:255
  soil **3**:195; **4**:255
  by waves **2**:142; **4**:*254*
  by wind **3**:185; **4**:255
estuaries **3**:181; **9**:670
  and pollution **2**:142
eurypterids **7**:558
evaporites **8**:598–599; **9**:687
evolution **4**:282–283, *283*; **5**:381
exosphere **1**:54; **5**:386
extinction **4:264–265**, 305; **6**:467
  and extraterrestrial impacts
    1:43; **2**:149; **3**:171, 173;
    4:264; **6**:467, 476
  Jurassic **5**:390
  Quaternary **9**:653
  Triassic **10**:758, 759

Fata Morgana **7**:495
faults **4:266–267**; **7**:*515*
  and metamorphic rocks
    6:475
fault traps **7**:*522*
feldspars **5**:366; **9**:673
fens **10**:793
ferromanganese **6**:437
fetch **10**:786
fires, grassland **5**:325
fish **3**:188, 189; **7**:496; **8**:*580*
fjords **2**:129, 142; **4**:254; **9**:*652*
flood basalt eruptions **10**:781
floods **3**:195; **4:272–273**; **9**:671
  biblical **5**:364
  flash **3**:184; **4**:272
Florida Current **5**:334
flowstone deposits **2**:110
fluorite *See* calcium fluoride
fluorspar *See* calcium fluoride
flutes **4**:312
fog **5**:349; **7**:*499*
fold mountains **7**:*515*
footprints, fossilized **4**:283–284
forests **4:278–281**; **10**:737, 761
fossil fuels *See* fuels, fossil
fossils **4:282–285**; **9**:686
  Cambrian **2**:*88*–89
  in caves **2**:108
  and continental drift
    8:622–623
  Cretaceous **3**:173
  Devonian period **8**:*580*
  and geologic timescale
    4:305, 306
  human **1**:22; **4**:283–284
  index **4**:305
  Jurassic **4**:*284*; **6**:467
  and limestone **6**:410, *411*
  magnetism **6**:431
  Mississippian **7**:496
  Ordovician **7**:*558*
  Paleozoic **8**:*580*
  Precambrian **8**:*635*
  Silurian **9**:*689*
  and supercontinents **2**:157;
    4:318
fronts, weather **2**:135; **6**:439;
    7:485; **9**:663; **10**:789
frost **5**:*360*, 361
fuels, fossil **1**:54; **4**:283;
    7:550–551
  burning **1**:75; **8**:573
  in continental shelves **2**:158
  See also coal; natural gas; oil,
    crude
Fujita–Pearson scale **10**:755,
    796

Volume numbers appear in **boldface type** followed by colons. Page numbers in **boldface type** refer to main articles and their illustrations. Page numbers in *italic type* refer to additional illustrations.

Gabbro **6:**427; **9:**672
Galápagos Rift **5:**359
galena **7:**491; **8:**564; **9:**693
gangue **8:**564, 565; **9:**692
gases, atmospheric **1:**52, 59; **2:**100
Geiger counters **8:**638
gemstones **4:300–301**; **9:**650, 700–701
See also crystals
geochemistry **4:**307
geodynamo **6:**431
Geographia **4:**302
Geographica **4:**302
geological surveys **5:**371
geologic timescale **4:304–305**, 306–307
geology **4:306–307**
geomorphology **5:**394
geophysics **4:**307; **8:**612
geysers **4:308–309**; **5:**331
Geysir **4:**309
glaciers **4:310–312**; **5:**361; **9:**653
  and cliffs **2:**129
  erosion by **4:**253–254, 311, 312; **5:**395
  and fjords **2:**129, 142; **9:***652*
  glacier caves **2:**110
  ice age **5:**362, 363, 364, 367
  and ice avalanches **1:**63
  and lake formation **5:**392
  and supercontinents **4:**318
  in valleys **2:**129, 142; **4:***306*, 307, 311
glauconite **9:**679
global warming **2:**101, 133, 140; **3:**195, 238; **4:313–315**
  and deserts **3:**185
  during the Cretaceous **4:**265
  and glaciers **4:**312
  and sea level **2:**157; **4:**312, 315
Glossopteris (seed fern) **8:***598*, 599, 622
gneiss **5:**381; **6:**475; **8:**635; **9:**650
gold
  gold rushes **1:**61; **4:***317*; **7:**494; **8:**565
  mining or panning for **4:**317; **6:**473; **7:**493, *494*; **8:**565
Gondwana **2:**89, 157; **4:318**; **5:**369, 390; **7:**558; **8:**582, 588, 589
  and Africa **1:**19
  and Antarctica **1:**33

  and Australia **1:**61
  gorges **4:**252; **6:**411; **10:**775
  Grand Bahama Banks **6:**411
  granite **3:**199–200; **5:**366; **6:**426, 427, 475; **7:**490
    boulders **9:***672*
  graptolites **7:**558; **9:**689
  grasses, Cenozoic **2:**112
  grasslands **5:324–325**; **10:**737
  gravitometers **8:**638
  Greeks, ancient **4:**302; **6:**439
  greenhouse effect **1:**54; **2:**133, 140; **4:**313–314
  Greenwich Meridian **6:**439
  groins **2:**143
  groundwater **5:329–333**, 357
  gulches **10:**775
  Gulf Stream **1:**50; **2:**131; **5:334**; **6:**442; **7:**542
  Gutenberg discontinuity **3:**201, 203
  gypsum **1:**78; **8:**598–599; **9:**687
  gyres **1:**49; **7:**543; **8:**576–577

Hadrosaurs **3:**173
hail **5:**361; **10:**790
half-life **4:**307; **9:**656
halides **7:**491
halite **8:**598–599
hardness, scale of **4:**301; **7:**491
headlands, coastal **2:**142; **4:**254
headwinds **5:**386
hematite **6:**431; **7:**491; **8:***564*, 565; **9:**665
  in sand **9:**679
hoarfrost **5:***360*
Holocene epoch **2:**112; **9:**652
hominids **2:**112
horns, mountain **4:**254
horsetails **8:**589
hot spots **5:**381; **7:**515; **10:**781
humans, early **1:**22; **2:**111; **4:**283–284
humidity **1:**25; **5:348–349**; **7:**484
  relative **5:**348–349; **7:**484, 486
humus **5:**325
hurricanes **1:**49; **2:***102*, 103; **4:**273; **5:350–351**; **7:***486*; **10:***790*
  and storm surges **5:**351; **7:**521
hydrologic/water cycle *See* water, cycle
hydrology **5:356–357**
  See also groundwater
hydrosphere **3:**201
hydrothermal vents **5:358–359**

Ibex rock series **7:**558
ice **5:360–361**
  avalanches **1:**63
  See also glaciers
ice ages **1:**50; **2:**113, 133; **4:**307, 310; **5:362–365**; **9:**652
  glaciers **5:**362, 363, 364, 367
  and sea levels **2:**141, 158
ice caves **2:**110
ice cores **2:**133
Iceland **5:**381
ice sheets **8:**581; **9:652–653**
ichthyosaurs **3:**173; **4:***282*; **5:**391; **6:**467
igneous rocks **2:**128–129; **3:**199–200; **5:366–367**; **9:**672, 673
illite **2:***127*
inland seas **5:372–373**
intertropical convergence zone (ITCZ) **9:**707; **10:**761
intrusions **6:**427
ionosphere **1:**54; **5:376–377**; **7:**487; **9:**658
iron, abundance **8:**564
ironstones, banded **1:**54
irrigation **3:***194*, 195; **5:***332*; **10:**785
islands **2:**143; **5:380–381**; **7:**541; **10:**780
isobars **5:**350–351; **6:**439; **7:**485
isostatic recovery **5:**363
isotherms **7:**485
isthmuses **2:**142
ITCZ (intertropical convergence zone) **9:**707; **10:**761

Jade **4:**300
Japanese Current **2:**131
jet streams **1:**53; **5:386–387**; **10:**788
jetties **2:**143
joints **5:**367
Juan de Fuca Ridge **3:**171; **5:**359

Jurassic period **4:***284*; **5:390–391**; **6:**467

Kaolinite **2:***127*
karst landscapes **2:**110; **6:***410*, 411

Labrador Current **1:**50
lagoons **2:**143; **5:**393
lakes **5:***329*, **392–393**
  in Africa **1:**21–22
  and climate **2:**131
  oxbow **5:**392; **9:**671
  salt lakes **1:**61; **5:**393
  See also inland seas
landforms **5:394–395**
La Niña **3:238**
lapidaries **4:**301
latitude **6:**439
  and climate **2:**130
  horse latitudes **10:**788, 796–797
Laurasia **1:**19; **2:**157; **4:**318; **7:**558; **8:**582, *588*, 589
Laurentia **3:**188
lava **3:**170, *202*; **4:**257; **5:**366, 367; **7:514–515**; **9:***672*; **10:***781*
  pillow **5:**367; **6:**427; **10:**780
  See also magma
lava caves **2:***108*, 110
layer lattice, of clay **2:**127
lead sulfide **9:**693
levees **4:**272; **9:**671
life
  beginnings of **2:**88
  on Earth **3:**199; **6:**478
  lightning and thunder **2:**137; **6:408–409**; **7:**531; **8:**617; **9:**704; **10:***789*, 790
lignite **2:**140
lime *See* calcium oxide
limestone **1:**78; **2:**109–110; **6:410–411**, 469; **9:**673, 687

Convection currents flowing through Earth's mantle.

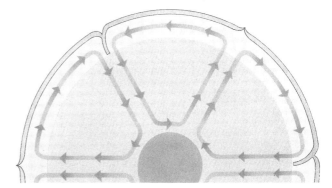

caves **2:**108, *109*–110; **5:**331; **6:**411

cliffs **2:**129

Mississippian **7:**496

pavements **6:***410*

uses **6:**411

limonite **9:**679

liquation **9:**665

lithosphere **3:**201; **8:**622

lodes **8:**564

lodestone **6:**432

loess **4:**255

Lomonosov Ridge **1:**40–41

longitude **6:**439

lungfish **3:**189

luster, mineral **7:**490–491

Lystrosaurus (reptile) **2:**157; **10:***759*

Mackerel sky **2:**136

magma **3:**170, 200; **5:**366–367; **6:***426*–**427**; **9:***672*; **10:**781

acid **5:**367

basic **5:**366–367

and metamorphic rock **6:**474–475

and ore formation **8:**564

and the rock cycle **9:**673

See also lava

magnesite **6:**429

magnesium, ores **6:**429

magnetic poles **6:430–431**; **8:**581

magnetic storms **6:**435

magnetism

Earth's **1:**58

paleomagnetism **8:**581

magnetite **6:***431*, 432; **7:**490; **8:**581

magnetosphere **6:**431, 435

Majasaura (dinosaur) **6:***466*

malachite **7:**490

mammals **2:**112, 157; **3:**173; **4:***265*; **10:**741

evolution **6:**467

mammoths **2:**111, *113*; **4:**284; **5:***362*; **8:**597

manganese

nodules **5:**369; **6:***437*; **8:**565

ores **6:**437

mantle, Earth's **3:**199, *201*, 202

convection currents **3:**202, *203*, 204

upper **6:**426

maps and mapping **4:**302, 303; **6:438–440**

ocean floor **6:**440, 442, 443

weather maps **5:**387; **6:**439; **7:**485

marble **1:**78; **3:**200; **6:***475*

Mariana Trench **6:**444; **7:**541, 545; **8:**576

discovery **7:**547

marine exploration **6:441–444**

marshes **10:**792–793

mass wasting **4:**255

meanders, river **4:**253

Mediterranean climate **2:**132

Mercalli scale **3:**206

Mercator's projection **4:**302; **6:***439*

mesosaurs **8:**582, 622–623

mesosphere **1:***52*, 53; **5:**386

Mesozoic era **4:**305; **6:466–467**

periods *See* Cretaceous period; Jurassic period; Triassic period

Tethys Sea **4:**257; **5:**373

metamorphic rocks **2:**129; **3:**200; **6:474–475**; **7:**490; **9:**673

metaquartzite **6:**475

meteorites **3:**171, 173, 203; **4:***265*; **5:**378; **6:**476–477; **10:**745

age **4:**305

and metamorphic rock **6:**475

meteoroids **3:**170, 171

meteorology **7:484–486**

See also weather

meteors **3:**170–171

methane

atmospheric **2:**137

forming clouds **2:**137

and prospecting **8:**638

mica **5:**366; **9:**673

micrite **6:**411

microscopes, petrological **7:**491

Mid-Atlantic Ridge **1:**48; **3:**171, 206; **5:**359; **7:**515, 534

discovery **6:**443

formation **1:**49; **4:**257; **5:**381

midnight sun **7:488**

midocean ridges **3:**201; **5:**381;**6:**427

aseismic **5:**369

Atlantic *See* Mid-Atlantic Ridge

faults **4:**266

Indian Ocean **5:**369

and ocean floor spreading **6:**431

volcanoes **3:**171

mineralogy **4:**307; **7:490–491**

See also crystals; gemstones

minerals **9:**673

evaporite **8:**598–599

hardness **4:**301

thermoluminescent **6:**418–419

See also prospecting

mining **7:492–494**

along fault zones **4:**267

aluminum ore **1:**31

in Antarctica **1:**34

on asteroids **1:**43

auger **2:**140

coal **2:**139–140; **7:***492*, 493

copper **3:**165

diamonds **4:**301

gold **4:**317; **6:***473*; **7:**493, *494*

the oceans **6:**444; **7:**493

petroleum **5:**369

strip **2:**140; **7:**493

See also prospecting

Miocene epoch **2:**112; **10:**740

Mississippian period **2:**138; **7:496–497**; **8:**588

mists **5:***348*, 349

Moho discontinuity **3:**201, 202

Mohs' scale **4:**301; **7:**491

monsoons **5:**369, 387; **7:506–507**; **9:**685; **10:**761, 797

montmorillonite **2:***127*

moraines **4:**312; **5:**363, 392; **9:**653

mountains **3:**200; **7:514–515**

and deserts **3:**184

formation **2:**113; **4:**267, 318; **5:**395; **7:514–515**; **8:**623

glaciers **4:**254

metamorphic rocks **6:**475

underwater **7:**515, 541

and the weather **3:**184; **9:***663*; **10:**790, 797

See also midocean ridges; volcanoes

mudslides/mudflows **3:**195; **4:**255, 273; **10:**781

mudstones **2:**126; **7:**558; **8:**589

mylonite **6:**475

National Centers for Environmental Prediction (NCEP) **7:**521

volcanoes **3:**171

National Earthquake Information Service **3:**206

National Weather Service (NWS) **5:**351; **7:**486, **520–521**

natural gas **7:**522, 551

under the oceans **1:***50*; **5:**369; **7:**493

nautiloids **7:**558

navigation **6:**433, 442

NCEP (National Centers for Environmental Prediction) **7:**521

Neogene period **10:**740

Ninety East Ridge **5:**369

nitrogen, atmospheric **1:**52

NOAA **7:**549

nodules

sea floor **5:**369; **6:***437*; **8:**565, 577

North American Plate **7:**534

North Atlantic Current/Drift **5:**334

northern lights *See* auroras

North Pole **7:**495

and the north magnetic pole **6:**430–431

nunataks **4:**311

Oases **5:***333*

obsidian **5:**366; **6:**427

ocean currents **2:**143; **7:**541, **542–543**

Atlantic Ocean **1:**49–50

and climate **2:**131

following **7:***548*

Gulf Stream **6:**442

Indian Ocean **5:**369

in the ocean depths **1:**50

Pacific Ocean **8:**576–577

tidal **10:**747

turbidity **2:**90, 91, 158

upwellings **1:**50; **3:**236; **7:**541, *543*

See also El Niño and La Niña; Gulf Stream

Ocean Drilling Project **5:**365; **7:**548

ocean floor **2:**156; **3:***200*–201; **7:**540–541

hydrothermal vents **5:358–359**

magma **6:**427

mapping **6:**440, 442, 443

mining **6:**444; **7:**493

spreading **6:**431; **8:**623

submarine canyons **2:**90, 91, 158; **6:**444

See also midocean ridges;

trenches, ocean
oceanography 7:546–549
oceans 3:200–201; 7:540–541
  and climate 2:131
  life in the depths 6:442–443
  mining 6:444; 7:493
  new oceans created 8:623
  pressure in 8:637
  temperatures 7:547
  water 5:356
  See also ocean floor; sea level
Ogallala aquifer 5:332
oil, crude (petroleum)
    7:550–551
  formation 1:54; 4:283; 7:522
  prospecting for 8:638
  under the oceans 1:50;
    2:158; 5:369; 7:493; 8:638
Old Faithful (geyser) 4:309;
    5:331
Oligocene epoch 2:112;
    10:740, 741
ooliths 6:410–411
opals 1:61; 4:301
Ordovician period 4:264–265;
    5:364; 7:558
ores 8:564–565
  radioactive 8:638
  See also prospecting
oxygen, atmospheric 1:52, 54;
    8:572, 581
ozone layer 1:51, 53; 3:199;
    4:313; 8:574–575; 10:724
  holes 1:33, 53; 6:407; 8:575;
    10:767

Pahoehoe 5:367
Paleocene epoch 2:112; 10:740
Paleogene period 10:740
paleomagnetism 8:581
paleontology 4:282, 307
Paleozoic era 4:305; 6:467;
    8:580–581
  See also under various periods
    of this era
Palm Sunday Tornado
    Outbreak 10:755
pampas 5:324; 10:737
Pangaea 3:172, 201; 4:318;
    8:582, 589, 622
  break up 1:19, 49; 3:172;
    4:318; 5:390; 8:582; 9:707;
    10:758–759
  climate 8:599
  formation 4:265; 7:497;
    8:598
  supercontinents formed
    from See Gondwana;

Laurasia
Panthalassa 8:598
pearls 4:300
peat 1:54; 2:139, 140; 8:589
peninsulas, coastal 2:142
Pennsylvanian period 2:138;
    8:588–589
peridotite 6:427
periods, geologic 4:304; 6:466
permafrost 8:596–597; 10:763
Permian period 4:265;
    8:598–599
petroleum See oil, crude
petrology 4:307
photosynthesis 1:54; 2:94, 101
pillow lava 6:427
pingos 8:597; 10:763
placer deposits 4:317; 8:564,
    565
plankton 7:522, 548
plants
  Cenozoic 2:112
  Cretaceous 3:173; 6:467
  Devonian 3:189
  Jurassic 5:391
  Mississippian 7:497
  Paleozoic 8:581
  Permian 8:598, 599
  Silurian 9:689
plate tectonics 2:157; 3:200,
    202; 8:582, 622–623
  and the Atlantic Ocean
    1:48–49; 2:102, 141, 157
  and Australasia 1:60
  and the Caribbean 2:102–103
  and coasts 2:141
  and continental shelves
    2:158
  and earthquakes 3:204
  and Eurasia 4:256
  and faults 4:267
  and Gondwana 4:318
  and the Indian Ocean 5:369
  and islands 5:380–381
  and metamorphic rocks
    6:475
  and mountain-building
    4:267; 5:395; 7:514, 515
  and the oceans 7:540; 8:623
  in the Pacific Ocean 8:577
  plate boundaries 8:623
  and volcanoes 10:780
Pleistocene epoch 2:112;
    5:392; 9:652, 653
plesiosaurs 3:173; 5:391; 6:467
Pliocene epoch 2:112; 10:740,
    741
points, coastal 2:142

polar regions 8:628–629
  climate 2:130, 132; 10:789
  daylight 3:179
  deserts 3:185
  glaciers 4:311
  seasons 9:684, 685
prairies 5:324
Pre-Archean eon 8:634
Precambrian time 2:88; 4:305;
    5:364; 8:580, 634–635
precipitation See rain, sleet,
    and snow
Prime Meridian 6:439
projections, mapmaking
    4:303; 6:439
prospecting 8:638
  for gold 6:473; 7:493, 494
Proterozoic eon 8:634
pterosaurs 3:173; 6:467
pumice 6:427
P waves 3:204
pyroclastic flow 5:367
pyrolusite 6:437
pyroxenes 9:673

Quartz 3:176; 4:300; 5:366;
    9:650, 673
quartzites 2:129
Quaternary period 2:112;
    9:652–653
  epochs 2:112
  ice age 2:113; 5:362, 364,
    392; 9:652
quicklime (calcium oxide) 1:78;
    6:411

Radar
  and depth of glaciers 5:361
  imaging tornadoes 10:755
  and weather forecasts 3:193;
    7:487, 521; 9:659
radioactivity, and dating rocks
    4:305, 307; 8:634
radiocarbon dating 2:108, 133;
    5:385; 8:612; 9:656–657
rain shadows 3:184; 9:663
rain, sleet, and snow
  (precipitation) 5:356, 357;
    7:485; 9:662–663;
    10:785, 789–790
  and air pressure 1:25
  and clouds 2:134, 135,
    136, 137; 5:356

and humidity 5:349
  monsoon rains 7:506, 507
  raindrops 9:663; 10:730, 789
  and seasons 9:685
  See also drought
rainwater, and weathering
    9:687
reefs, coral See coral reefs
remote sensing 9:668–669
  satellites 9:669
reptiles 3:173; 8:589, 599
reservoir rocks 7:522
reservoirs 5:393
rhyolite 6:426, 427; 9:672
rias 10:775
rice paddies 4:314
Richter scale 3:206
Ridge Inter-Disciplinary
    Global Experiments 7:548
rift valleys 4:266; 5:393,
    394–395; 10:774
Ring of Fire 3:205; 4:267;
    8:623; 10:780
rivers 9:670–671
  and canyons 2:90–91
  deltas 2:143; 3:180–181; 9:671
  deposition by 3:180–181;
    4:253; 9:671
  erosion by 4:252, 253; 9:671
  floods 4:272; 9:671
  and lake formation 5:392–393
  and landforms 5:395; 10:775
  river valleys 5:395; 10:775
  and sedimentary ores 8:565
rivulets 4:253
Robinson's projection 4:303
rock crystal 9:650
rock pedestals 5:395
rock phosphate 1:78
rocks 9:672–673
  dating 4:304–305, 307; 6:431;
    8:634; 9:656
  See also geology; igneous
    rocks; metamorphic rocks;

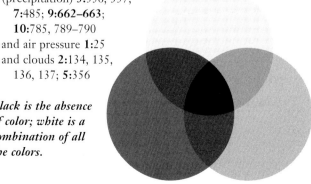

Black is the absence of color; white is a combination of all the colors.

sedimentary rocks
rock salt **8**:598–599; **9**:687
rubies **4**:*300*, 301

Salt domes **7**:*522*
San Andreas Fault **3**:205;
    4:266, *267*; **7**:534; **8**:623
sand **9**:**678–679**
sandbars **2**:143; **3**:180; **9**:679
sand-seas **3**:185
sandstone **3**:200; **6**:475; **7**:490;
    8:589; **9**:*679*, 687
  caves **2**:111
  quartz **7**:558
  Triassic **10**:759
sapphires **4**:301
sauropods **3**:173; **5**:391
savanna **5**:324, *325*
schist **6**:475
scintillometers **8**:638
sea caves **2**:111; **4**:254
sea-floor spreading **6**:431;
    8:623
sea levels
  and global warming **2**:157;
    4:312, 315; **9**:652
  past **2**:141, 158; **8**:581
  and trade winds **3**:237
seamounts **5**:380; **7**:541
seas **7**:540
  inland *See* inland seas
sea scorpions **7**:558
seasons **2**:130; **3**:203; **4**:250;
    9:**684–685**
  See also midnight sun
sea stacks **4**:254
seat earths **8**:589
sedimentary rocks **2**:129;
    3:200; **5**:395; **9**:672–673,
    686–687
  fossils **4**:282
  See also limestone
sediments **3**:180, 181; **5**:395;
    9:686
  continental shelf **2**:158
sediment traps **4**:285
seismic waves **3**:204, 206
seismographs **8**:638
seismology **9**:705
shales **2**:126; **4**:284; **7**:558
sheet silicate **2**:127
silica (silicon dioxide) **6**:426
silicates **7**:491; **9**:673
silicon **9**:679
sills **5**:367; **6**:427, 474–475
Silurian period **3**:188; **9**:**689**
sink holes *See* swallow holes
slaked lime (calcium

hydroxide) **1**:78; **6**:469
slate **6**:475; **9**:650
smogs **7**:531; **8**:574, 631
snow **5**:361; **9**:*662, 663*;
    10:790
  avalanches **1**:*62–63*
snowstorms, lake-effect **2**:131
soil
  erosion **3**:195; **4**:255
  pollution in **8**:631
soil creep **4**:255
solar wind, and auroras **1**:59;
    6:431, 435
southern lights *See* auroras
South Pole **1**:32
  and the south magnetic pole
    6:431
specific gravity, of minerals
    7:491; **9**:673
Spindletop oil field **7**:551
spits, coastal **2**:143
springs **5**:330
  hot *See* geysers
stalactites and stalagmites
    2:*101*, 108, 110; **5**:331
starfish, fossil **7**:*558*
steppes **5**:324
storm surges **5**:351; **7**:521
straits **5**:372
strata **8**:564; **9**:673, 686
stratigraphy **4**:307
stratopause **10**:724
stratosphere **1**:*52*, 53; **5**:386;
    10:724
  See also ozone layer
streak, mineral **7**:490
streamers **6**:409
stromatolites **8**:*635*
subarctic region **2**:132
subduction **2**:158; **4**:257, 267;
    6:427; **8**:623
subtropics **2**:132
  deserts **3**:184
sulfides **7**:491; **8**:638
Sun
  sunlight and climate **2**:130–131
  See also midnight sun; solar
    wind
Sunda Trench **5**:369
swallow holes (sink holes;
    dolines) **2**:*109*, 110
swamps **10**:792, *793*
S waves **3**:204

symmetry, crystal **3**:176, *177*
synclines **7**:515

Taiga **4**:279; **10**:762
tailwinds **5**:386
talc, hardness **7**:491
tar **7**:550
tectonic plates *See* plate
  tectonics
Tektite II (underwater project)
    7:549
temperate regions **2**:132;
    10:**736–737**
  forests **4**:280; **10**:737
  grasslands **5**:325; **10**:737
  seasons **9**:*684*, 685; **10**:736
temperature(s)
  atmospheric **7**:484
  lowest on Earth **1**:33
Tertiary period **2**:112, 113;
    10:**740–741**
Tethys Sea **2**:157; **4**:257;
    5:373, 390; **8**:598; **10**:741
theodolites **6**:440; **10**:796
thermosphere **1**:*52*, 53–54;
    5:386
thorium **8**:638
thunder *See* lightning and
  thunder
thunderstorms **2**:135; **6**:408
tidal waves (tsunamis) **3**:173,
    205; **4**:273; **10**:**744–745**,
    781, 787
tides **7**:509; **10**:**746–747**
  and coastal erosion **2**:142
  spring and neap **10**:747
tillites **5**:363–364
TIROS 1 (satellite) **2**:137;
    7:*485*, 521
titanosaurs **5**:*390*
topaz **4**:300, *301*
tornadoes **3**:193; **7**:*520*, 521;
    10:**754–755**, 790
trade winds *See* winds, trade
travertine **6**:411
trenches, ocean **3**:201, 203;
    4:267; **7**:*541*, 545; **8**:623;
    10:774
triangulation **6**:440
Triassic period **6**:467;
    10:**758–759**
trilobites **2**:*88–89*; **6**:467;
    7:558; **9**:*689*

tropical regions **2**:132; **4**:280
    5:324; **9**:685; **10**:**760–761**,
    788
  See also monsoons; winds,
    trade
tropopause **10**:724, 796, 797
troposphere **1**:52, 53; **2**:134;
    5:386; **10**:724
tsunamis *See* tidal waves
tuff **4**:284; **5**:366
  welded **5**:367
tundra **1**:74; **2**:132; **8**:*597*;
    10:**762–763**
turquoise **4**:300
typhoons **4**:273; **5**:350

Uhuru (satellite) **4**:261
United States Geological
  Survey (USGS) **10**:768
updrafts **10**:795
upwellings **1**:50; **3**:236; **7**:541,
    543
uranium **8**:638
USGS (United States
  Geological Survey) **10**:768

Vaiont Dam **4**:273
valleys **10**:**774–775**
  formed by glaciers **4**:*306*,
    307; **9**:652; **10**:775
  hanging **4**:254; **10**:775
  rift **4**:266; **5**:393, 394–395;
    10:774
  U-shaped **4**:254; **5**:363, 395;
    10:762, 774, 775
  V-shaped **4**:253; **5**:394, 395;
    10:774
  See also canyons; trenches,
    ocean
vegetation
  and altitude **2**:*131*; **4**:278
  See also forests; plants
veld **5**:324; **10**:737
volcanic plugs **5**:*366*
volcanoes **10**:**780–781**
  and climate **2**:133
  craters **3**:*170*
  Cretaceous **4**:265
  of Eurasia **4**:257
  formation **3**:203; **7**:514–*515*;
    8:623; **10**:*781*
  forming islands **5**:381; **7**:515;
    10:780
  lava **3**:*202*; **5**:367; **7**:514–*515*
  and magmas **6**:426, 427
  Tertiary period **10**:*741*
  tunnels and caves **2**:110
  underwater **3**:171; **5**:381;

Volume numbers appear in **boldface type** followed by colons. Page numbers in **boldface type** refer to main articles and their illustrations. Page numbers in *italic type* refer to additional illustrations.

7:515, 534; **10**:781
See also Ring of Fire

Wadis **4**:254; **9**:670; **10**:775
water **10**:784–785
cycle **3**:194; **5**:329, 356, *357*;
7:540; **9**:662; **10**:784–785,
789
on Earth **3**:199, 200
from forests **4**:280
freezing point **5**:361
surface **5**:357
underground *See*
groundwater
See also glaciers; humidity;
hydrology; ice; lakes;
oceans; rivers
waterfalls **4**:252; **9**:671
waterspouts **10**:754
water table **5**:330, 357
waves (sea) **2**:143; **10**:786–787
and coastal erosion **2**:142;
4:*254*
tidal (tsunamis) **3**:173, 205;
4:273; **10**:744–745, 781, 787
wave trains **10**:745
weather **2**:130; **10**:788–790
and El Niño and La Niña
3:236–238
fronts **2**:135; **6**:439; **7**:485;
9:663; **10**:789
maps **5**:387; **6**:439
National Weather Service
(NWS) **5**:351; **7**:486,
520–521
oceans influencing the **7**:547
See also climate; clouds;
lightning and thunder;
meteorology; rain, sleet,
and snow; seasons; winds
Weather Bureau **7**:521
weather forecasts **1**:25; **7**:485,
486, 520–521, 547
and radar **3**:193; **7**:487, 521;
9:659
monsoons **7**:507
weathering **5**:395; **8**:565; **9**:687
wells **5**:331, 357
artesian **5**:331
westerlies **5**:386; **10**:788, 797
wetlands **10**:792–793
and pollution **2**:142
whirlpools, in the oceans **7**:549
whirlwinds **10**:754
Whiterock rock series **7**:558
white smokers **5**:359
williwaws **8**:576
wind cells **10**:797

winds **1**:51; **10**:788, 790,
795–797
causing ocean currents **7**:*543*
and the Coriolis effect **1**:25;
10:790, 795
and El Niño **3**:236–237, *238*
erosion by **3**:185; **4**:255
scales **10**:755, 796
trade **1**:22, 25, 49; **3**:236,
237, 238; **5**:387; **8**:576;
10:761, 788, 797
See also hurricanes; jet
streams; monsoons;
tornadoes
wind vanes **10**:796

X rays, and mineralogy **7**:491

Zechstein Sea **8**:599

ENVIRONMENT

Acid rain **1**:75; **5**:357; **7**:531;
8:631; **9**:693
and coal **2**:140
Agent Orange, herbicide **5**:336
aluminum, recycling **1**:*31*;
8:565
Antarctic Treaty **1**:34
Arctic region, hole in the
ozone layer over **8**:575

Biodegradation **10**:757
bioremediation **1**:*70*
bunds **1**:13

Carbon, cycle **1**:54
carbon dioxide
and deforestation **4**:279, 313
and global warming **1**:54;
2:101, 140; **4**:279,
313–314
catalytic converters **2**:*105*;
4:*313*
CFCs *See* chlorofluorocarbons
Chernobyl **4**:271; **9**:*654*
chlorofluorocarbons (CFCs)
1:33; **5**:337
environmental effects **1**:53,
75; **4**:*314*; **5**:337; **8**:*574*,
575, 601
coal, environmental effects

2:140
coasts
pollution **2**:142
protection **2**:143
converters, catalytic **2**:*105*;
4:*313*
coral reefs, threats to **2**:*103*

DDT **5**:336
deforestation **4**:*279*, 313;
5:357; **10**:761
dialysis **10**:757
dioxins **1**:70; **5**:336; **8**:601

Energy
new sources of **7**:551
from the oceans **6**:444
estuaries, and pollution **2**:142
Exxon Valdez oil spill **1**:70;
8:631

Fertilizers **1**:75; **2**:103; **7**:531;
8:631
flotation, of toxic waste
10:756–757
foods, genetically modified
(GM) **1**:73
forests, deforestation **4**:*279*,
313; **5**:357; **10**:761
fuels, fossil, burning **1**:75

Genetic engineering **1**:70, 73
Global Ocean Ecosystem
Dynamics Program **7**:548
global warming **2**:101, 133,
140; **3**:195, 238;
4:313–315
Cretaceous **4**:265
and deserts **3**:185
and glaciers **4**:312
and sea level **2**:157;
4:312, 315

greenhouse effect **1**:54; **2**:133,
140; **4**:313–314

Hydrology **5**:356–357

Inland seas, shrinking
5:372–373

Joint Global Flux Study **7**:548

Landfills **8**:621; **10**:757
logging, and deforestation
4:279
Love Canal **10**:757

Mercury (metal), in the
environment **6**:459
metals
pollution by **8**:630
scrap **8**:565; **9**:665
methane, and global warming
4:313, *314*
mining, in Antarctica **1**:34
Montreal Protocol **8**:575

Night vision binoculars **5**:340
nitrogen
cycle **7**:*531*
fixation **7**:531
nitrous oxide, a greenhouse gas
4:*313*
nuclear wastes **10**:757

Oil, crude (petroleum), spills
1:70; **8**:*631*
overfishing, and coral reefs
2:103
oxygen, cycle **8**:*572*
ozone **1**:53; **6**:407; **8**:572

***The rain shadow on the
leeward side of a mountain.***

ozone layer **1**:51, 53; **3**:199; **4**:313; **8:574–575**
and CFCs **1**:53, 75; **5**:337
holes **1**:33, 53; **6**:407; **8**:575; **10**:767

PCBs (polychlorinated biphenyls) **1**:70; **8:587**; **10**:757
pesticides **1**:70; **5**:357; **8**:630
petroleum *See* oil, crude
phosphates, in detergents **3**:187
plastics
 degradable **8**:621
 recycling **8**:*621*
pollution **1**:75; **8:630–631**
 air **3**:233; **8**:574–575, 630, 631; **9**:*693*; **10**:724
 and bioremediation **1**:*70*
 chlorinated pollutants **1**:70
 coastal **1**:*70*; **2**:*142*
 control **8**:631
 detergents **3**:187
 from fertilizers **1**:75; **7**:531; **8**:631
 and global warming **2**:133; **4**:315
 light **8**:630
 and marine life **7**:548
 metal **8**:630
 noise **1**:13–14; **8**:630
 oil/petroleum spills **1**:*70*; **8**:*631*
 by ozone **8**:574–575
 PCBs **1**:70; **8**:587
 pesticides **5**:357; **8**:630
 soil **8**:631
 water **5**:333, 357, 393; **8**:631; **10**:785
 See also acid rain; toxic waste

Rain, acid *See* acid rain
recycling **1**:*31*; **8**:565, *621*

Sedimentation, of toxic waste **10**:756
Silent Spring (book) **5**:336
slag heaps **10**:*757*
smogs **7**:531; **8**:574, 631
sulfur, removal from fuels **8**:601
sulfur dioxide **5**:357; **8**:631; **9**:*693*
sulfuric acid, and acid rain **5**:357; **9**:*693*

TCDD **5**:336
thermometers **5**:341

tides, and coastal erosion **2**:142
tin **9**:665
tourism, and coral reefs **2**:*103*
toxic waste **3**:175; **10:756–757**

Ultraviolet radiation, and ozone **1**:52, 53; **6**:407; **8**:575; **10**:767
Union Carbide factory disaster **8**:601

Waste, toxic *See* toxic waste
water
 conservation **5**:332–333
 cycle **3**:194; **5**:329, 356, *357*; **7**:540; **9**:662; **10**:784–785, 789
 from forests **4**:280
 pollution **5**:333, 357, 393; **8**:631; **10**:785
waves (sea), and coastal erosion **2**:142
wetlands
 and pollution **2**:142
 protecting **10**:793

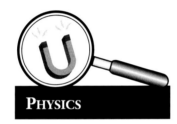

PHYSICS

Absolute zero **3**:174; **4**:293; **5**:339–340; **10**:743
acceleration
 due to gravity **5**:327–328
 and force **4**:277; **6**:453; **7**:512
accumulators (rechargeable batteries) **1**:65; **3**:216
acoustics **1**:12–14; **9**:705
 See also sound
aerodynamics **1:15–18**
air, compressed **6**:441
airfoils **1**:18
airplanes
 aerodynamics **1**:15, *16–17*
 motion **7**:*513*
 pressurized cabins **1**:24
air resistance (drag) **1**:15

alpha particles **1**:57; **5**:385; **7**:526; **9**:654–655; **10**:726
alternating current (AC) **3**:213
amperes (amps) **3**:214
anechoic chambers **1**:14
aneroid cells **1**:24
anions **5**:374; **9**:646
antimatter **3**:226; **8**:584–585, 586; **10**:727
antiquarks **8**:586
Appleton layer **5**:377
atoms **1:55–57**
 and the Big Bang **10**:770
 and color **2**:145
 electrons in **1**:56; **2**:107, 145; **3**:227–228, 234–235; **5**:396–397; **6**:418; **8**:*583*, 584
 nucleus *See* nucleus, atomic structure *See* subatomic structure
 See also fission, nuclear; fusion, nuclear

Barographs **1**:*23*, 24
barometers **5**:349; **6**:458; **7**:485
batteries **1:64–65**; **3**:214, *215*; **10:742–743**
 long-life (alkaline) **1**:65
 rechargeable **1**:65; **3**:216
 zinc–carbon (dry cells) **1**:64–65
beta decay **5**:385; **7**:526; **9**:655
bicycles **6**:454; **7**:*512*
bimetallic strips **10**:739
binoculars **6**:407
 night vision **5**:340
blue-shift **1**:67; **3**:193
boiling *See* evaporation and boiling
bridges, designed **3**:211
bubble chambers **3**:*227*; **8**:*585*, 586

Caloric **5**:341
calories **5**:339
capacitors **3**:230
capillary action **2:92–93**
capillary effect **2**:93
carbon, isotopes **2**:97, 108; **5**:384, 385; **9**:654, 655, *656–657*

carbon dating *See* radiocarbon dating
cathode rays **2:106–107**
cathode-ray tubes **2**:106, *107*; **3**:225, 231
cations **5**:374; **9**:646
CAT scans **10**:798
Celsius temperature scale **5**:339, 341; **10**:739
centigrade *See* Celsius temperature scale
centrifuges **2**:*114*, 115; **7**:499
 ultracentrifuges **1**:69
centripetal and centrifugal forces **2:114–115**
 at the equator **3**:199
chain reactions **4**:270
 and fusion **4**:288
charge-couple devices (CCDs) **10**:735
Chernobyl **4**:271; **9**:*654*
chromatography **2**:93
circuits
 electric **1**:64; **3**:213
 electronic **3**:229–330
cloud chambers **3**:226
coal-fired power plants **3**:215
color **2:144–147**; **3**:218; **6**:404; **7**:553
 photography **2**:147; **3**:197; **8**:*605*
compasses, magnetic **6**:430, 433; **8**:638
Compton effect **9**:649
condensation **8**:606; **10**:784
condensers **4**:259
conductance, electrical **3**:213
conduction, heat **4**:247; **5**:340
conductors, electrical **1**:31; **3**:213, 215; **9**:701
 and temperature **10**:738–739
contact forces **4**:276, *277*
convection (heat) **4**:247; **5**:340
 and the weather **7**:485
 See also convection currents
convection currents, air **5**:*339*, 340
cosmic rays **1**:53; **3**:166–167, 226
cryogenics **3:174–175**
cryosurgery **3**:175
cyclists, aerodynamics **1**:*15*, 18
cyclotrons **3**:235

Dead rooms **1**:14
deceleration **4**:277
decibels **1**:14
density **1**:25; **3:182–183**
deserts, mirages in **7**:*495*

Volume numbers appear in **boldface type** followed by colons. Page numbers in **boldface type** refer to main articles and their illustrations. Page numbers in *italic type* refer to additional illustrations.

deuterium, and fusion 4:288–289
dew point 2:134; 5:349
diffraction
 light 6:406; 7:554, *556*
 sound 1:12; 9:705
diffusion 3:190–191; 4:294–295
 See also osmosis
dimensions 9:708; 10:752, 753
 compacted/invisible 4:276
diodes 3:230, 231; 9:688
 light-emitting (LEDs) 3:230;
 4:247
direct current (DC) 3:213
discharge tubes 2:106;
 3:220–221; 4:295
distillation 4:259
domains 5:378; 6:435
doping 9:688
Doppler effect 3:192–193
 and astronomy 1:47; 3:193;
 10:769
drag 1:15, 17
dry ice 8:606; 9:*701*
dynamo, Earth as a 6:431

Earth, infrared images of
 5:*370*
echoes 1:12, 13; 9:704
echolocation 10:764
elasticity 3:210–211
electricity 3:212–215, 229
 conductors and insulators
 3:213; 9:701
 electrostatics 3:212–213,
 232–233
 from fuel cells 5:355
 from geysers 4:309
 lightning a form of 6:408–409
 and magnetism *See*
 electromagnetism
 superconductors 3:175;
 10:739
 See also batteries; power
 plants
electrocardiographs 2:107
electrodes 1:*64*
electromagnetic induction
 3:223
electromagnetic spectrum
 3:218–221; 5:370
 and remote sensing
 9:668–669
 See also gamma rays; infrared
 radiation; light;
 microwaves; radio waves;
 ultraviolet radiation;
 X rays

electromagnetism 3:222–224;
 4:276; 6:433–434; 8:611
 particles carrying 8:585
electromagnets 2:107; 3:*222*,
 223–224; 6:436
electromotive force (EMF)
 3:223
electronegativity 8:627
electronics 3:229–231
electrons 3:225–228
 in atoms 1:56; 2:107, 145;
 3:227–228, 234–235;
 5:396–397; 6:418, 434;
 8:*583*, 584
 behaving as waves 3:227, 228
 charge 3:227
 discovery 1:56; 2:107; 3:225;
 8:584; 10:725
 and electricity 3:213, 215
 and lasers 5:396–397
 and luminescence 6:418
 mass 1:56
 orbits/shells/energy levels
 5:396–397; 8:584; 9:714
 positive *See* positrons
 in semiconductors 9:688
 See also electronics
electrostatics 3:212–213, **232–233**
elevators, and weight 10:791
energy 4:244–248
 internal 4:246–247
 kinetic 3:215; 4:246, *247*,
 248; 5:339
 law of conservation of 4:245,
 246, 248; 8:611; 10:743
 from the oceans 6:444
 potential 3:215; 4:245, *247*,
 248
 See also fission, nuclear;
 fusion, nuclear
engines, jet 6:453
entropy 10:743, 753
equivalence, principle of 5:328
ether (hypothetical medium)
 9:709
evaporation and boiling
 4:258–259
 boiling 4:258, *259*; 6:*415*,
 457
 evaporation 4:258–259; 5:348,
 356; 8:606
expansion, thermal 9:700
eyes, vision 2:145–146;
 7:552–553, *555*

Farenheit temperature scale
 5:339, 341; 10:739
fatigue 3:211

ferromagnetism 5:378; 6:434–435
fiber optics 4:268–269; 7:556
fiberscopes 4:*269*
fission, nuclear 4:248,
 270–271, 289
 See also fusion, nuclear
flight, aircraft 1:*16*–17, *18*
fluid dynamics 1:17–18
fluorescence 3:219; 6:419
flywheels 7:505
focal length 10:733–734
force multipliers 6:454
forces 4:274–277
 and particles 8:585
 See also electromagnetism,
 gravity; strong nuclear
 force; weak nuclear force
free falling 10:*791*
freezing, cryogenic 3:175
frequency 3:218, 221; 9:703;
 10:764
friction 4:274, **286–287**
fulcrums 6:*454*
fusion, latent heat of 5:341
fusion, nuclear 3:235; 4:248,
 288–289; 8:617
 in the Sun/stars 4:*288*; 5:327;
 6:450; 7:536; 9:664, 694

Galvanometers 6:434
gamma rays 3:221; 5:385;
 8:638; 9:655
 and positrons 3:226
 and remote sensing 9:669
gases 4:292–295; 6:*451*; 9:700
 density 3:183
 diffusion 3:190, 191;
 4:294–295
 gas laws 4:292, 293, 294;
 8:608–609, 637
 gauge bosons 8:585, 586
gears 6:454, 455
Geiger counters 3:166, 167;
 8:638
generators 3:224; 6:434
geophysics 4:307; 8:612
gluons 8:585, 586; 10:727
gravitation, universal
 constant of 4:275
gravitons 8:585
gravity 4:274–276; 5:326–328;
 7:527; 8:612
 acceleration due to
 5:327–328
 artificial 5:328

and black holes 1:76; 9:667
carrier particles for 8:585
Earth's 3:199; 4:*275*; 5:*328*
law of universal gravitation
 4:275; 5:326–327; 7:513,
 528–529
 and motion 5:327; 7:513
 in space 9:710, *711*; 10:791
 See also relativity, general
 theory of
gyroscopes 7:505

Hadrons 8:586
heat 4:248; 5:338–341; 10:738
 and friction 4:286
 heat capacity 5:340
 history of the study of 5:340,
 341
 and internal energy 4:246–247
 kinetic theory of 5:341
 latent 5:340–341; 8:606
 radiation *See* infrared
 radiation
 solar 5:341
 transference 4:247;
 5:338–339, 340
 See also temperature(s);
 thermodynamics
helium, and fusion 4:*288*–289;
 6:450
Hertz 9:703
holography 5:343–345, 398
Hooke's law 3:210
Hubble Space Telescope
 5:346–347; 7:*555*
 mirror 7:554, 555
hydroelectricity 3:215; 4:*244*
hydrogen
 and fusion 4:288–289; 6:450
 isotopes 4:288–289; 5:354
hydrometers 3:183
hypersonic speeds 1:17

Ice, melting point 6:*457*
ideal gas law 4:293, 294; 8:609,
 637

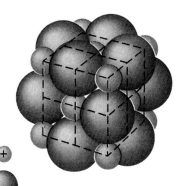

***Crystal structure of common
salt (sodium chloride).***

inertia **6**:450, 452; **7**:504, 512
infrared radiation **2**:144;
 3:*219*, 220; **5**:340,
 370–371; **6**:404
 discovery **1**:47; **3**:219; **5**:370
 and the greenhouse effect
 4:313
 uses **5**:340, 371; **9**:668, 669
infrasound **10**:764
instruments, musical **9**:703–704
insulators
 electrical **3**:213, 215; **9**:701
 heat **5**:339, 371
intensity, sound **9**:703
interference
 light waves **5**:*344*;
 6:405–406; **7**:554, 556
 sound waves **1**:12–13; **9**:*703*,
 705
ions, in the ionosphere **5**:376
iron and steel, magnetism
 5:378–379; **6**:434–436
isotopes **3**:235; **5**:384–385;
 7:526, 539; **8**:593; **9**:654
 carbon **2**:97, 108; **5**:384,
 385;**9**:654, 655, *656–657*
 cosmogenic **9**:656–657
 hydrogen **4**:288–289; **5**:354
 nuclear spin **7**:539
 and positron emission **3**:226;
 5:385; **9**:655
 radioactive (radioisotopes)
 5:385; **9**:654
 tellurium **6**:*471*
 uranium **3**:235; **4**:295;
 5:384–385; **7**:526; **9**:656

Jacks **6**:*453*; **8**:637
Joule–Kelvin Effect **10**:743
joules **5**:339
Joule–Thomson Effect **3**:174

Kelvin temperature scale
 5:339–340, 341; **10**:739,
 743
 absolute zero **3**:174; **4**:293;
 5:339–340; **10**:743
Kennelly–Heaviside layer
 5:377
kinetic theory **5**:341; **10**:743
kinetic theory of gases **4**:292–294

Large Electron–Positron
 Collider **8**:586
lasers **2**:145; **5**:396–398; **7**:556
 and holography **5**:343–345,
 398
 laser fusion **4**:289

LEDs (light-emitting diodes)
 3:230; **4**:247
lenses **7**:*554*; **10**:733–734
leptons **8**:585, 586; **10**:727
levers **6**:453, *454*, 455
lift **1**:16–17, 18
light **2**:144; **3**:220; **6**:404–407;
 7:*552–554*
 brightness **6**:405
 colors in white light
 2:144–145; **3**:218; **7**:*528,
 529, 553*
 diffraction **6**:406; **7**:554, *556*
 and the Doppler effect **3**:193
 interference **5**:*344*;
 6:405–406; **7**:554, 556
 monochromatic **2**:145; **5**:396
 as particles **3**:227; **6**:405;
 7:553; **8**:602
 photoelectric effect **8**:602
 polarized **3**:177; **5**:383; **6**:417
 red- and blue-shift **1**:67;
 3:193
 reflected **2**:145; **6**:405, *407*;
 7:*552*
 refraction **6**:406–407; **7**:495,
 553, 554
 and relativity **9**:666–667
 speed **3**:218; **6**:404, *405*, 407;
 7:552; **8**:611–612;
 9:666–667, 709
 ultraviolet See ultraviolet
 radiation
 and vision **7**:552–553, *555*
 wavelength **2**:144, 145;
 3:218; **6**:404, *405*; **7**:553;
 9:715
 wave–particle duality **6**:405;
 7:529, 553, 557
 as waves **3**:218; **6**:*405*; **7**:553,
 557
 See also color; holography;
 lasers; mirages; optics;
 photons; rainbows
lights
 electric **3**:214; **4**:*246*; **6**:406
 fluorescent **6**:419; **8**:617
 neon **4**:*295*
liquids **4**:292; **6**:414–415, *451*;
 9:700
 capillary action **2**:92–93
 density **3**:183
 diffusion in **3**:191

See also evaporation and
 boiling; melting and
 boiling points
lodestone **6**:432, 433
loudspeakers **4**:247; **9**:703

Machines **6**:453–455
magnetic declination **6**:430
magnetic inclination **6**:430
magnetic resonance imaging
 (MRI) **3**:224; **7**:*539*
magnetism **5**:378–379;
 6:432–436; **9**:701
 and electricity See
 electromagnetism
 and polarity **8**:627
magnetohydrodynamics
 (MHD) **6**:436
magnetometers **6**:446; **8**:638
magnetrons **7**:487
Manhattan Project **4**:271
masers **7**:487
mass **3**:182; **5**:327; **6**:450
 relation to energy **4**:271;
 6:450
matter **6**:451
 "dark" **6**:451; **10**:771
 shadow **4**:276
 wave-particle duality **9**:648,
 649
mechanics **6**:452–455
 See also gravity; momentum;
 motion
melting **8**:606
melting and boiling points
 6:457
mesons **4**:276; **8**:585
microphones **4**:247; **9**:703
microscopes **3**:*228*; **7**:*554*
microwaves **3**:220; **7**:487
 9:669
mirages **7**:495, 554
mirrors **7**:553, 554
momentum **7**:504–505
Moon, rainbows around **9**:661
motion **7**:512–513
 Newton's laws of **2**:114, 115;
 4:274, 277; **5**:327;
 6:452–453; **7**:504, 512–513
 relative **9**:666
 rotational **6**:455
motors **3**:224; **4**:247; **6**:434
Munsell system **2**:147

muons **3**:167; **8**:586

Neutrinos **8**:586
neutrons **1**:57; **3**:234, 235;
 7:526, 539
 discovery **7**:526, 539; **8**:584;
 10:726
 particles comprising **10**:727
Newtonian/classical physics
 7:527–529; **8**:609,
 610–611; **9**:648, 708
night vision binoculars **5**:340
noise, measurement **1**:14
nuclear magnetic resonance
 (NMR) **7**:539
nuclear physics **7**:538–539; **8**:613
 See also fission, nuclear;
 fusion, nuclear
nuclear power **4**:271
nucleons **7**:539
nucleus, atomic **1**:56; **3**:234,
 235; **7**:526
 discovery **1**:57; **3**:227–228;
 7:538–539; **10**:726
 forces in **4**:276–277; **8**:585;
 10:726–727

Optics **6**:404–405; **7**:529,
 552–557
 fiber optics **4**:268–269; **7**:556
Optiks (book) **7**:529
oscilloscopes, cathode-ray
 2:*106*, 107
osmosis **8**:568–569

Particle accelerators **7**:*538*;
 8:585–586; **10**:725, 727
particle physics **8**:583–586, 613
 antimatter **3**:226; **8**:584–585,
 586; **10**:727
 discovery of electrons **1**:56;
 2:107; **3**:225; **8**:584;
 10:725
 discovery of neutrons **7**:526,
 539; **8**:584; **10**:726
 discovery of protons **9**:646
 and fundamental forces
 8:585
 gauge bosons **8**:585, 586
 particle accelerators **7**:*538*;
 8:585–586; **10**:725, 727
 quarks **4**:277; **8**:586, 613;
 10:727
 standard model **8**:586
 viewing particle tracks See
 bubble chambers; cloud
 chambers
 See also cosmic rays;

Volume numbers appear in **boldface type** followed by
colons. Page numbers in **boldface type** refer to main
articles and their illustrations. Page numbers in *italic type*
refer to additional illustrations.

subatomic structure
pascals **1:**25
periscopes **6:**407
permeability, magnetic **6:**435
phase change **5:**341
phosphor **2:**107
photocells **3:**215; **8:***602*
photoconductivity **8:**602
photoelectric effect **8:602**;
  9:649
photoemission **8:**602
photometers **2:**147
photons **2:**145; **6:**405; **7:**553;
  8:584, 602
  are carrier particles **8:**585,
    586
  and lasers **5:**396, 397
  and luminescence **6:**418
photovoltaic effect **8:**602
physical change **8:606–607**
physics **8:610–613**
  geophysics **4:**307; **8:**612
  nuclear **7:538–539**; **8:**613
  space **9:**711
  See also Newtonian/classical
    physics; particle physics
piezoelectricity **10:**765
pi-mesons **8:**585
planets, and gravity **1:**46;
  4:274–275
plasma **4:**289; **8:617**
  and MHD generators **6:**436
plastic deformation **3:**210
Plato **7:**556
plutonium **4:**271; **8:626**;
  10:783
p-n junctions **9:**688
polarity **8:627**
positrons **3:**226; **5:**385; **7:**526;
  8:585; **9:**655; **10:**727
powder, density **3:**183
power **6:**454
power plants **3:**215, 233; **4:**259
  nuclear **4:**270; **8:***626*
pressure **1:**25; **8:636–637**
  of gases **4:**292–294; **8:**636–637
Principia Mathematica (book)
  1:46; **7:***527*, 528
prisms, and light **2:***144*; **3:**218;
  5:370; **6:**406–407; **7:***528*,
  529, 553; **9:**661, 715
protons **1:**57; **3:**234, 235;
  7:538, 539; **9:646**
  mass **9:**646
  particles comprising **8:**586;
    10:727
pulleys **6:***455*
P waves **3:**204

Quanta **3:**227; **8:**612; **9:**648,
  649, 714
quantum chromodynamic
  (QCD) force **8:**585
quantum mechanics **3:**228;
  8:609, 612
quantum theory **7:**527; **8:**584;
  9:648–649
quarks **4:**277; **8:**586, 613;
  10:727
quartz, piezoelectricity **10:**765

Radar **1:**47; **9:***659*
  Doppler **3:**192, 193; **9:**659
  images of Venus **6:**424–425
  police speed guns **3:**192, 193
  and remote sensing **9:***668–669*
  and weather forecasts **3:**193;
    7:487, 521; **9:**659
radiation (electromagnetic) *See*
  electromagnetic spectrum
radiation (heat) **4:**247; **5:**341
radiation (ionizing)
  cosmic **3:166–167**
  detection **3:**166
radioactivity **4:**277; **7:**539;
  9:654–655, 656
  alpha decay **5:**385; **7:**526;
    9:654–655
  beta decay **5:**385; **7:**526;
    9:655
  carbon **2:**97
  and dating rocks **4:**305, 307
  detection **3:**166
  discovery **4:**270; **8:***612*;
    9:655
  and gamma rays **3:**221;
    8:638; **9:**655
  and neutron capture **7:**526
  and nuclear waste **10:**757
  positron emission **3:**226;
    5:385; **7:**526; **9:**655
  See also fission, nuclear;
    isotopes; radiocarbon
    dating
radiocarbon dating **2:**108, 133;
  5:385; **8:**612; **9:656–657**
radioisotopes **5:**385; **9:**654
radio waves **3:**219–220; **5:**377;
  9:658–659
  AM transmission **5:**377;
    9:658–659
  detection on Venus **6:**446
  FM transmission **9:**658–659
  and the ionosphere **5:**376,
    377; **9:**658
  See also radar; telescopes,
    radio

radium **9:**655
rainbows **2:**144, *145*; **6:**407;
  9:660–661
ramps **6:**454–455
reactors **4:**271, 289
red-shift **1:**47, 67; **3:**193;
  9:651, 716
reflection **6:**405; **7:***552*
  reflecting telescopes **7:***557*;
    10:733
  total internal **4:**268; **6:**406
refraction
  index of **4:**268
  law of **7:**557
  light **6:**406–407; **7:**495, *553*,
    554
  and mirages **7:**495
  and rainbows **9:**660–661
  refracting telescopes
    10:732–733, 734
  sound wave **9:**705
  total internal **6:**406–407
relativity **7:**527; **9:666–667**
  and electromagnetism **6:**434
  general theory of (theory of
    gravity) **4:**275–276; **5:**327,
    328; **8:**612; **9:**667
  special theory of **8:**611–612;
    9:666–667; **10:**752–753
remote sensing **9:668–669**
resistance, electrical **3:**213
resistors **3:**230
resonance **9:**704
retina **2:**145–146
reverberations **1:**13, 14
rotational motion **6:**455
rubber **3:**211

Scattering, light **7:**523
scientific method **8:**613
screws **6:**454–455
seawater, ships powered using
  6:436
seesaws **6:***454*
seismic waves **3:**204, 206
seismometers **3:**206
semiconductors **9:688**
ships
  floating **3:***182*,
    183
  friction **4:**287
  powered using
    seawater
    6:436

skyscrapers, designed **3:**211
smoke, diffusion **3:***190*
Snell's law **7:**557
solar constant **5:**341
solar wind **5:**376
solenoids **6:**436
solidification **8:**606
solids **4:**292; **6:***451*
  diffusion in **3:**191
  melting points **6:**457; **9:**701
sonar **3:**192; **6:**443; **9:***705*;
  10:765
sonic boom **9:***704*
sound **9:702–705**
  and the Doppler effect **3:***192*
  infrasound **10:**764
  and light **6:**419
  recording **9:**705
  speed **6:**409; **9:**704
  used for prospecting **8:**638
  waves **1:**12–13; **8:**638; **9:**702,
    703, 704–705
  See also acoustics; ultrasound
sound chambers **1:***13*
South Pole, mirages at **7:**495
space-time continuum **9:**709
specific heat capacity **5:**340
spectrographs **9:**715
spectrometers **9:***714*, 715
spectroscopy **9:**649, **714–15**
spectrum, light **2:***144*; **3:**218;
  7:553; **9:**661, *715*
speed **7:**513
state, change of **8:***606*
strain **3:**211
stress **3:**210–211
strong nuclear force **3:**235;
  4:276–277; **8:**585; **9:**646
subatomic structure **1:**56–57;
  7:539; **10:725–727**
  Bohr model **3:**228; **8:**584;
    9:649; **10:**726

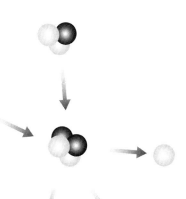

Helium 3 nuclei fuse to form a helium 4 nucleus, two protons, and lots of energy.

discovery of electrons **1**:56; **2**:107; **3**:225; **8**:584; **10**:725

discovery of neutrons **7**:526, 539; **8**:584; **10**:726

discovery of the nucleus **1**:57; **3**:227–228; **7**:538–539; **10**:726

discovery of protons **9**:646

nuclear atom model **1**:57; **3**:227–228; **7**:538–539; **8**:584, 612; **10**:726

plum pudding model **1**:56; **2**:107; **7**:538; **8**:584; **10**:725

quarks **4**:277; **8**:586, 613; **10**:727

subatomic forces **4**:276–277; **8**:585; **10**:726–727

See also particle physics

sublimation **2**:100; **5**:361; **8**:606; **9**:*701*

submarines **4**:271; **8**:637

Sun
bending light **9**:*667*
energy from **4**:245; **5**:341
nuclear fusion **4**:*288*; **6**:450; **9**:694
rainbows around **9**:*661*
See also solar wind

superconductors **3**:175; **10**:739

superfluidity **3**:175

supersonic speeds **1**:15, 17; **9**:*704*

superstring theory **4**:276

surface tension **2**:92–93; **3**:186; **10**:730

S waves **3**:204

swings, energy **4**:*247*

Tau particles **8**:586

telescopes **7**:557; **10**:732–735
cosmic ray **3**:167
first **1**:45; **7**:557; **10**:*734*
Galilean **10**:733, *734*
infrared **5**:371
radio **9**:*658*; **10**:732, 734–735
reflecting **7**:557; **10**:733
refracting **10**:732–733, 734
reflector-refractor **10**:733

televisions, cathode-ray tubes **2**:106, *107*

temperature(s) **5**:338; **10**:738–739
absolute zero **3**:174; **4**:293
cryogenic **3**:174–175
measuring **5**:339–340, 341

scales **5**:339, 341; **10**:738, 739
See also heat

thermal conductivity **5**:339

thermodynamics **4**:248; **8**:609, 611; **10**:742–743

thermograms **5**:*338*

thermometers **5**:341; **10**:739

Three Mile Island **4**:271

thrust **1**:17

timbre **9**:703

time, dilation **10**:753

tires, friction **4**:287

tokamaks **4**:289

torus **4**:289

trains **1**:15; **4**:287
maglev **6**:*436*

transducers **4**:247

transformers **3**:215, 224

transistors **3**:230, 231; **9**:688

translucency **6**:405

transparency **6**:405

trees, deciduous **10**:761

triodes **3**:231

turbines **10**:*742*, 765

Ultrasound **10**:764–765
uses **3**:193; **9**:705; **10**:*764*, 765

ultraviolet radiation **2**:144; **3**:219, *220–221*; **6**:404; **10**:766–767
and fluorescence **3**:219
and free radicals **5**:375
and ozone **1**:52, 53; **6**:407; **8**:575; **9**:669; **10**:767
uses **10**:767

uncertainty principle **9**:649

unified field theory **4**:276

universal gravitation **4**:275; **5**:326–327; **7**:513, 528–529

uranium
enriched **4**:295; **5**:384–385
isotopes **3**:235; **4**:295; **5**:384–385; **7**:526; **9**:656
nuclear fission **4**:270–271

Vacuums **5**:339

vacuum tubes **3**:231

Van de Graaff generators **3**:*233*

vapor pressure **4**:258, 259; **5**:349

vapor(s) **4**:*294*
water **1**:25, 52; **5**:348, 349; **7**:*500*

vector quantities **4**:277

vectors **7**:*513*

velocity **7**:513

Very Large Array (VLA) **10**:735

viscosity **4**:287

voltaic pile **1**:65; **3**:214, 215

Water
boiling point **4**:258, *259*; **6**:457; **8**:*606*; **10**:784
properties **10**:784
specific heat capacity **5**:340
states **6**:457; **8**:*606, 607*; **10**:784
vapor *See* vapor(s), water

wavelengths
electromagnetic **2**:144; **3**:*221*; **6**:404
light **2**:144, 145; **3**:218; **6**:404; **7**:553

wave–particle duality
light **6**:405; **7**:529, 553, 557
matter **9**:648, 649

weak nuclear force **4**:277; **8**:585

weight, and mass **5**:327; **6**:450

weightlessness **10**:791

welding **4**:*293*; **8**:617

whispering galleries/chambers **1**:*14*

wind tunnels **1**:*17*

work **4**:244–245

W particles **8**:585, 586

X rays **3**:177, 221; **10**:798

Yamoto (water craft) **6**:436

Z particles **8**:585, 586

SPACE SCIENCE

Aerobraking **6**:425

aerospace planes **7**:519

Volume numbers appear in **boldface type** followed by colons. Page numbers in **boldface type** refer to main articles and their illustrations. Page numbers in *italic type* refer to additional illustrations.

Agena (space vehicle) **4**:297, 298

air showers **3**:167

alloys, made in space **9**:711

Alpha Centauri system **1**:66

Altair **2**:155

Andromeda Galaxy **2**:155

Andromedids **6**:477

Apollo missions **1**:35–39; **4**:275; **6**:*422–423*; **7**:510, *511*, 518
IMPs **4**:261

Ariel (moon) **10**:*773*

asteroids **1**:42–43; **3**:171; **6**:477; **9**:696
asteroid belts **1**:*42*, 43; **2**:148; **9**:696, *698*

astronauts
and centrifugal forces **2**:*114*, 115
and gravity **5**:328; **10**:791
women **6**:463

astronomical units (AUs) **9**:697

astronomy **1**:44–47
See also constellations; telescopes

ATDA **4**:298

Atlantis (space shuttle) **7**:*519*; **9**:713

Atlas rockets **4**:299; **6**:*462*, 464

Atmospheric Explorers **4**:261

Aurora 7 (spacecraft) **6**:465

AUs (astronomical units) **9**:697

Betelgeuse **2**:155

Big Bang **1**:47; **3**:169; **4**:261; **5**:342, 354, 355; **9**:709; **10**:727, 770, 771

binary stars **1**:66–67; **3**:209; **7**:536; **9**:716–717; **10**:794

biology, space **9**:710–711

black holes **1**:67, **76–77**; **4**:261, 291; **5**:327, 347; **7**:537; **9**:*666*, 718; **10**:771
and gravity **1**:76; **5**:327; **9**:667
and quasars **9**:651
and time travel **10**:753

blue-shift **1**:67; **3**:193

brown dwarfs **10**:771

Callisto (moon) **5**:388, 389; **9**:680, 698

celestial equator **4**:250, 251

celestial poles **2**:154

celestial sphere **4**:250

Cepheid variables **1**:47

Ceres (asteroid) **1**:42; **9**:696

Challenger (space shuttle) **7:***518*, 519
charge-couple devices (CCDs) **10:**735
Charon **8:**624–625; **9:**699
Chiron **9:**696
chondrites **6:**478
Clementine (space probe) **6:**423; **7:**510; **9:**669
clusters, galaxy **4:**290, 291
Columbia (space shuttle) **9:***711*
comets **1:**42; **2:148–149**; **9:**697
  meteoroids from **6:**478
constellations **2:152–155**; **4:**250; **9:**716, 717, 718
Cosmic Background Explorer (COBE) **4:**261
cosmic dust collectors **6:**446
cosmic rays **1:**53; **3:166–167**, 226
cosmology **3:168–169**
COSTAR **5:**347
Crab Nebula **9:***647*
Crab Pulsar **9:***647*
crystals, grown in space **9:**711
Cygnid meteors **6:**477
Cygnus X-1 **1:**77

Days **3:178–179**, 203
  solar **2:***84*; **3:**178
Deimos (moon) **1:**43; **6:**449; **9:**680
Deneb **2:**154, 155
Discovery (space shuttle) **5:**347
docking, in space **4:**297–298
Doppler effect, and astronomy **1:**47; **3:**193; **10:**769
dust, interplanetary **6:**477

Earth **3:198–203**; **9:**695
  distance from the Sun **9:**697
  orbit **2:***86*; **3:**203
  eclipses **3:208–209**
    lunar **3:**200, 209; **7:***509*
    solar **3:***208–209*; **7:**509
  ecliptic **2:**153, 155; **4:**250
  electrons, cosmic ray **3:**167
Endeavour (space shuttle) **5:**347
  epicycles, theory of **1:**45
  equator, celestial **4:**250, 251
  equinoxes and solstices **2:***86*; **3:**179; **4:249–251**; **9:***685*
  eras **2:**87
  ergospheres **1:**77
  "Eskimo" nebula **9:***717*
Europa (moon) **5:**388, 389; **9:**680, 698; **10:**783
event horizon **1:**77
Explorer probes **4:260–261**

Extreme Ultraviolet Explorer (EUVE) **4:**261

F*aith* 7 (spacecraft) **6:**465
Freedom 7 (spacecraft) **6:**464, 465
free falling **10:***791*
Friendship 7 (spacecraft) **6:**465
fusion, nuclear **3:**235; **4:288–289**
  in the Sun/stars **4:***288*; **5:**327; **6:**450; **7:**536; **9:**664

Galaxies **3:**169, 193; **4:290–291**; **10:**770
  quasars are? **9:**651
  See also Milky Way
Galilei, Galileo
  astronomical observations **1:**45; **3:**169, 198; **7:**509, 525; **9:**708
  telescope **10:**733, *734*
Galileo (space probe) **1:**43; **5:**389; **7:***508*, *517*, 519
gamma rays **10:**729
Ganymede (moon) **5:**388, 389; **9:**680, 698
Gaspra (asteroid) **1:**43
Geiger counters **3:**166, 167
Gemini missions **4:296–299**; **7:**518
geoids **4:**261
GEOS satellites **4:**261
Giacobini–Zinner, Comet **4:**261
gravitational slingshot **10:**782
gravity **4:**274–6; **5:326–328**
  and black holes **1:**76; **5:**327
  in space **9:**710, *711*

Hale–Bopp comet **2:***149*
Halley's Comet **2:**149; **8:**616
heliopause **9:**695
helium, in the Universe **7:**532
Hertzsprung–Russell diagram **1:**47
Horsehead nebula **7:**523
Hubble Constant **5:**347
Hubble Space Telescope **3:**169; **4:***290*; **5:346–347**; **7:**519, *555*; **8:***624*; **9:**669; **10:**735
  mirror **7:**554, 555
Huygens (space probe) **9:**683
hydrogen, in the Universe **7:**532

I*apetus* (moon) **9:**683
Ida (asteroid) **1:**43

inflation **10:**770
Infrared Astronomical Satellite (IRAS) **10:**735
Infrared Space Observatory **9:**669
International Space Station (ISS) **7:**519; **9:**710, *712*, 713
International Sun-Earth Explorers (ISEEs) **4:**261
International Ultraviolet Explorer (IUE) **4:**261; **10:**735
interplanetary dust **6:**477
Interplanetary Monitoring Platforms (IMPs) **4:**261
Io (moon) **5:**388, 389; **9:**680, 698; **10:**783
ion chambers **6:**446

Jupiter **5:388–389**; **9:**697
  comet collisions with **2:**149; **9:**697
  day length **3:**179
  Galileo probe to **1:**43; **5:**389; **7:***517*
  moons **1:**45; **5:***388*, 389; **9:**680, 698; **10:**783
  Pioneer probes to **8:***616*
  Voyager probes to **5:**389; **10:**783

Karnak, Temple of **1:**44
Kuiper Belt **1:**43; **8:**625; **9:**699

Lacertids **6:**477
Liberty Bell 7 (spacecraft) **6:***464*, 465
light-years **4:**290, 291; **7:**489
Low Earth Orbit (LEO) **9:**681
lunar missions **6:420–423**; **7:**510
  Apollo **1:**35–39; **4:**275; **6:***422–423*; **7:**510, *511*, 518
Lunar Orbiter program **6:**422; **7:**510
Lunar Prospector (space probe) **6:**423; **7:**510
lunar roving vehicle (LRV) **1:**39; **6:***421*, 423
Lunar Surveyor (space probe) **6:**423
Luna space missions **6:**420–421, 423; **9:**675
Lunik space missions **7:**510
Lunokhod (robot rover) **6:**423

MACHOs **10:**771
Magellan (space probe) **6:424–425**; **9:**669
Magellanic Clouds **4:**291; **10:**771
magnetometers **6:**446
magnetosphere **6:**431
Mariner probes **6:**424, **445–447**; **10:**776, 778
Mars **3:**198, 199; **6:**447, **448–449**; **9:**696
  atmosphere **6:**448; **10:**779
  distance from the Sun **9:**697
  life on **10:**779
  Mariner probes to **6:**445–446, 447; **10:**778
  Mars probes to **9:**675
  meteorites from **6:**449, 477
  moons **1:**43; **6:***449*; **9:**680
  surface **6:**448–449; **9:**696
  temperature **6:**448; **10:**779
  Viking probes to **6:***448*; **10:778–779**
matter **6:**451
  dark **6:**451; **10:**771
Mercury (planet) **3:**179, 198, 199; **6:460–461**; **9:**695
  day length **6:**460
  distance from the Sun **9:**697
  Mariner probe to **6:**445–446, *447*
  temperature **6:**447, 460; **9:**695

Double wall of a thermos flask stops heat transfer.

Mercury missions **1**:36; **4**:296; **6**:462–465; **7**:518

meteorites **3**:171, 173, 198, 203; **4**:265; **5**:378; **6**:476–477

age **4**:305

impact on Mercury **6**:461

from Mars **6**:449, 477

thermoluminescent **6**:419

meteoroids **3**:170, 171; **6**:476, 477–478

meteors **3**:170–1; **6**:476–478

meteor showers **6**:477, 478

meteor streams **2**:149

microgravity **9**:710, 711; **10**:791

Milky Way **1**:77; **4**:290, 291; **7**:489; **9**:664, 709; **10**:769

mining, on asteroids **1**:43

Mir (space station) **9**:713

Miranda (moon) **9**:698; **10**:773

months, lunar **2**:84; **7**:508–509

Moon **7**:508–511; **9**:695

and calendars **2**:84–85

craters **3**:171, 198; **7**:509, 510

eclipse of **3**:200, 209; **7**:509

far side **6**:420; **7**:510

gravity **3**:199; **5**:327

missions to *See* lunar missions

orbit **5**:328

seas (maria) **7**:509–510, 511

and tides **7**:509; **10**:746–747

water on **6**:423

moonquakes **7**:511

moons **9**:680

multiple mirror telescopes (MMTs) **10**:735

NACA **7**:516

NASA **7**:516–519

See also Apollo missions; Gemini missions; Hubble Space Telescope; Mercury missions; space probes

NEAR (Near-Earth Asteroid Rendezvous) **1**:43

nebulas **3**:169; **4**:291; **7**:523; **9**:647, 717, 717

Neptune **7**:524–525; **9**:697, 698

moons **7**:525; **8**:625; **9**:681, 698–699; **10**:783

Voyager probe to **7**:524, 525; **9**:681; **10**:783

Nereid (moon) **7**:525

neutrons, cosmic ray **3**:167

neutron stars **1**:76; **5**:327; **7**:537; **9**:647, 718

pulsars **9**:647

Next Generation Space Telescope (NGST) **5**:347; **10**:735

North Star *See* Polaris

novas **1**:67; **7**:536–537

supernovas **1**:76; **3**:166, 167; **4**:261; **7**:536–537; **9**:718

nutation **4**:251

Oberon (moon) **10**:773

occultation **3**:209

Olympus Mons **6**:449

Oort Cloud **2**:148; **9**:699

Orbiter (space shuttle) **1**:17

Orion Nebula **2**:155

Parallax **1**:46; **9**:708, 716

Phobos (moon) **1**:43; **6**:449; **9**:680

Phoebe (moon) **9**:683

physics, space **9**:711

Pioneer program **8**:614–616

Pioneer Venus missions **6**:424

planetesimals **8**:625; **9**:699

planets

day length **3**:179

formation **9**:699

and gravity **1**:46; **4**:274–275

orbiting the Sun **1**:45, 46; **3**:169; **5**:326; **9**:697

See also Solar System

Planet X **8**:624; **9**:699

plasma **8**:617

solar **10**:728, 729

See also solar wind

Pleiades **2**:155

Pluto **5**:347; **7**:525; **8**:624–625; **9**:695, 697

distance from the Sun **9**:697

plutonium **10**:783

Polaris (Pole Star; North Star) **2**:154; **6**:430, 432; **9**:717

Pole Star *See* Polaris

Population I and II stars **7**:489

protons, cosmic ray **3**:167

pulsars **9**:647

Quasars **1**:77; **4**:291; **9**:651; **10**:770

and cosmic rays **3**:167

Radar, images of Venus **6**:424–425

radioisotope thermal generators (RTGs) **10**:783

radiometers

infrared **6**:446

microwave **6**:446

radio waves, detection on Venus **6**:446

Ranger space program **6**:421–422

red giants **1**:66; **7**:536, 537; **9**:664, 718

red-shift **1**:47, 67; **3**:193; **9**:651, 716; **10**:769

Redstone rockets **6**:464

regolith **1**:43; **7**:510

remote sensing **9**:668–669

satellites **5**:371; **9**:669

rocks, Moon **6**:419, 423

Russian space missions **9**:674–675

race for the Moon **1**:36; **9**:675

space stations **9**:674, 710, 712, 713

Sagittarius A* **7**:489

Salyut missions (space stations) **9**:674, 710, 712, 713

satellites **9**:680–681

batteries in **1**:64

Explorer probes **4**:260–261

first **1**:35; **7**:516

infrared imaging from **5**:370, 371; **10**:735

and mapmaking **6**:440, 443

natural **9**:680

remote-sensing **5**:371; **9**:669

solar panels **1**:64

telescopes on **10**:735

Saturn **9**:682–683, 697

day length **3**:179

distance from the Sun **9**:697

moons **9**:669, 680, 683, 698; **10**:783

rings **9**:683, 697; **10**:783

Voyager probes to **9**:682, 683; **10**:783

Saturn V (rocket) **1**:36, 37; **6**:422

scattering, light **7**:523

Schwarzschild radius **1**:77

Seyfert galaxies **4**:291

Shoemaker–Levy 9 comet **2**:149

sidereal period **7**:508

Sigma 7 (spacecraft) **6**:465

singularities **1**:77

Sirius **2**:85

system **1**:66; **10**:794

Skylab (space station) **7**:518; **9**:710, 712–713

slingshot, gravitational **10**:782

solar panels **1**:64; **6**:446

Solar System **1**:52; **3**:198; **7**:489; **9**:694–699

See also asteroids; comets; meteors; planets; Sun

solar wind **5**:376; **8**:617; **9**:695; **10**:728

and auroras **1**:59; **6**:431, 435

spectrometers to measure **6**:446

solstices *See* equinoxes and solstices

Soyuz spacecraft **1**:36; **9**:674

space **9**:708–709

space race **1**:35; **6**:462

space science **9**:710–711

See also weightlessness

space shuttles **7**:518–519

space sickness **9**:711

space stations **5**:328; **7**:518, 519; **9**:712–713

See also International Space Station; Salyut missions; *Skylab*

Space Telescope Science Institute **5**:346

space-time continuum **9**:709; **10**:753

space walks **4**:297, 298, 299; **9**:675

spectrometers, solar plasma **6**:446

Sputnik missions (satellites) **4**:260; **7**:516; **9**:674, 681

stars **9**:716–718

becoming black holes **1**:76–77

binary (double) **1**:66–67; **3**:209; **7**:536; **9**:716–717; **10**:794

blue **7**:489, 537; **9**:716, 717, 718

brightness **1**:47, 67; **2**:153; **9**:717

distances **1**:46, 47

eclipsed **3**:209

Volume numbers appear in **boldface type** followed by colons. Page numbers in **boldface type** refer to main articles and their illustrations. Page numbers in *italic type* refer to additional illustrations.

elements from **3:***234, 235*
failed **5:**388
formation **9:**717; **10:**770
mass **1:**67; **9:**717
moving relative to Earth **1:**67; **3:**193
neutron *See* neutron stars
nuclear fusion in **5:**327
Population I and II **7:**489
red **9:**716, 717
red giants **1:***66*; **7:**536, *537*; **9:664**, 718
shooting *See* meteors
white dwarfs **1:**67, 76; **7:**523, *536*, 537; **9:**718; **10:**794
yellow **9:**716, 718
See also constellations; galaxies; novas; pulsars; Sun
Sun **9:**694–5; **10:728–729**
formation **9:***696*
helium **5:**342
magnetic field **6:***435*
nuclear fusion **4:***288*; **6:**450; **9:**694; **10:**729
sunspots **6:**435; **10:**728, *729*
See also solar wind; stars
superclusters, galaxy **4:**290, 291
supernovas **1:**76; **4:**261; **7:**536–537; **9:**647, 718
and cosmic rays **3:***166*, 167
Surveyor program **6:**422; **7:**510
Surveyor 3 **1:***38*; **6:**422, 423
synthetic aperture radar (SAR) **6:**424–425

Telescopes
cosmic ray **3:***167*
first **1:**45; **7:**557; **10:***734*
infrared **5:**371; **10:**735
See also Hubble Space Telescope
Tharsis Rise **6:**449
time travel **10:752–753**
Titan (moon) **9:**669, 680, 683, 698; **10:**783
Titan II rockets **4:**296, 297, 299
Titania (moon) **10:***773*
transient lunar phenomena (TLPs) **7:**511
Triton (moon) **7:**525; **8:**625; **9:***681*, 698–699; **10:**783
Trojans (asteroids) **1:**43; **9:**696

Umbriel (moon) **10:***773*
Universe **10:769–771**

beginning *See* Big Bang
"dark matter" **6:**451; **10:**771
expanding **1:**47; **3:**169, 193; **4:**291; **5:**347; **10:**769, 770, 771
infinite number **10:**753
shape **10:**771
study of *See* cosmology
Uranus **1:**46; **3:**209; **7:**525; **9:**697–698; **10:772–773**
Voyager probe to **3:**209; **10:**772, 773, 783

Van Allen belts **4:**260; **8:**617
Vanguard rockets **4:**260; **7:**516
Vega (star) **2:**155; **4:**251
Venera probes **6:**424; **9:**675; **10:**777
Venus **3:**198, 199; **9:**695; **10:776–777**
atmosphere **6:**424, 425; **9:**695; **10:**776, 777
atmospheric pressure **6:**447
day length **3:**179; **10:**776
distance from the Sun **9:**697; **10:**776
Magellan probe to **6:424–425**
Mariner probes to **6:**424, 445–447; **10:**776
Pioneer missions to **6:**424; **8:***614*
surface **6:**425; **10:**777
temperature **6:**424, 446, 447; **10:**776
Venera missions to **6:**424; **9:**675; **10:**777
Venus Orbiting Imaging Radar (VOIR) **6:**424
Viking probes **6:***448*; **10:778–779**
voids **4:**291
Vostok spacecraft **9:**674, 675
Voyager Interstellar Mission **10:**783
Voyager probes **3:**209; **5:**389; **7:***524*, 525; **9:***681*, 682, *683*; **10:**772, 773, **782–783**

Weightlessness **10:**791
white dwarfs **1:**67, 76; **7:**523, *536*, 537; **9:**718; **10:**794
WIMPs **10:**771
wormholes **1:**77; **10:**753

X rays, from space **1:***44*, 77; **4:**261

Years
leap **4:***250*

solar **2:**84

Zodiac **2:**155; **4:**250
Zond spacecraft **1:**36; **9:**675

Accumulators (rechargeable batteries) 1:65
acoustics **1:12–14**
aerodynamics **1:15–18**
aeronautics, and NASA **7:**519
airbags, automobile **4:**263
air conditioning **5:**349
airplanes
aerodynamics **1:**15, *16*–17
aerospace planes **7:**519
aluminum **1:**31
contrails **2:**137
flight **1:***16*–17, *18*
noise **1:**14
pressurised cabins **1:**24
use of radar **7:**487
air (atmospheric) pressure, measuring **1:***23*, 24, 25; **7:**485
airships **3:**183; **5:***354*
Alvin (submersible) **6:**444
ambrotyping **8:**604
anechoic chambers **1:**14
anemometers **10:**796
aneroid cells **1:**24
angina, treatment **4:**263
aqualungs **6:**441
architecture, and acoustics **1:**13
automobiles
aerodynamics **1:**16, *17*, 18
airbags **4:**263
batteries **1:**65
catalytic converters **2:***105*; **4:***313*
fuel cells **5:**355
ignition **6:**436
jacks **6:***453*

spraying **3:**233
starter motor **6:**436

Bakelite **8:**619
barcode readers **5:**398
barographs **1:***23*, 24
barometers **1:**24, 25; **6:**458; **7:**485
bathyscaphes **6:**444
bathyspheres **6:**443–444; **7:**547
batteries **1:64–65**; **3:**214, *215*; **10:**742–743
long-life (alkaline) **1:**65
rechargeable **1:**65; **3:**216
zinc–carbon (dry cells) **1:**64–65
bicycles **6:**454
binary code **3:**231
binoculars **6:**407
blast furnace **2:***118*; **5:***378*, *379*; **6:**458, 473; **9:**692–693
bombs
hydrogen/thermonuclear **4:**289
nuclear **1:**59; **4:**270, *271*, 289
brighteners **6:**419
bubble chambers **3:***227*

Calculators **3:***229*, 230
LCD displays **6:**417
cameras **7:**554; **8:***604*
camera obscura **8:**603
infrared **5:**371
Schmidt **10:**733
capacitors **3:**230
carving rigs **7:**493
cathode rays **2:106–107**
cathode-ray tubes **2:**106, *107*; **3:**225, 231
CAT scans **10:**798
CD players **5:**398; **7:**556
celluloid **8:**619
centrifuges **2:***114*, 115; **7:**499

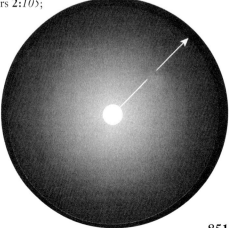

A black hole with its center and radius (called the Schwarzschild radius) shown.

ultracentrifuges **1**:69
charge-couple devices (CCDs)
    10:735
chronometers **3**:179; **10**:751
circuits
    electric **1**:64; **3**:213
    electronic **3**:229–*230*
    integrated *See* integrated
        circuits
clocks **10**:*749*–751
cloud chambers **3**:226
coal gas **2**:139
communications, and fiber
    optics **4**:269
computers **3**:229, 230
    binary code **3**:231
    modeling the weather **7**:547
    and oceanography **7**:549
    optical **4**:269; **7**:556
    screens **6**:*416*, 417, 419;
        7:556
    and weather forecasts **7**:486
Concorde (aircraft) **1**:14, 17
crops, spraying **3**:233
cryogenics **3**:**174–175**
cryosurgery **3**:175
cyclonite (RDX) **4**:263

Daguerreotypes **8**:603–604
dams **4**:272–273; **5**:393
dead rooms **1**:14
Deep Flight (submersible) **7**:549
Deep Rover (submersible) **7**:549
Deepstar 4000 (submersible)
    6:*444*
diodes **3**:230, 231
    light-emitting (LEDs) **3**:230;
        4:247
discharge tubes **2**:106;
    3:220–221; **4**:295
distance, measured using lasers
    5:398
distillation
    of coal tar **2**:139
    destructive **2**:138–139
diving **6**:*441–442*, 444; **7**:547
    and helium **5**:342
diving bells **5**:369
diving suits **7**:547
dynamite **7**:493

Electricity
    from geysers **4**:309
    solar **3**:215
    See also power plants
electrodes **1**:*64*
electromagnets **2**:107; **3**:222,
    223–224; **6**:436

electronics **3**:**229–231**
electron microprobes **7**:491
engines **5**:345; **6**:453
Explorer probes **4**:**260–261**
explosives **4**:**262–263**
    for mining **7**:492–493
    to discover oil fields **7**:551

Fabrics, brighteners **6**:419
fiberglass **8**:621
fiber optics **4**:**268–269**; **5**:398
fibers, synthetic **10**:**731**
fiberscopes **4**:*269*
flashlights **1**:64

Galvanometers **6**:434
gears **6**:454
Geiger counters **3**:166, 167;
    8:638
generators **3**:224; **6**:434
GLORIA (sonar device) **9**:*705*
gravitometers **8**:638
gunpowder **4**:*262*, 263;
    7:492–493
gyroscopes **5**:347

Headphones **1**:14
heart disease, treatment **4**:263
helicopters, flight **1**:*18*
holography **5**:343–345, 398
hourglasses **10**:749
Hubble Space Telescope **3**:169;
    4:*290*; **5**:**346–347**; **7**:*555*
hydrometers **3**:183

Industrial Revolution, and
    coal **2**:138
integrated circuits (silicon
    chips; computer chips)
    2:*125*; **3**:*231*
Interplanetary Monitoring
    Platforms (IMPs) **4**:261
ion chambers **6**:446

Jacks **8**:637
jet fighters, cockpit noise **1**:14

Kaiko (bathyscaphe) **6**:444

Lamps
    fluorescent **6**:419
    infrared heat **5**:371
    ultraviolet "sun" **10**:767

See also lights, electric
lasers **2**:145; **5**:**396–398**; **7**:556
    and holography **5**:*343–345*,
        398
    laser fusion **4**:289
LCDs (liquid crystal displays)
    6:*417*; **7**:556
LEDs (light-emitting diodes)
    3:230; **4**:247
lights
    electric **3**:214; **4**:*246*; **6**:406
    fluorescent **6**:419; **8**:617
    neon **4**:*295*
liquid crystal displays (LCDs)
    6:*417*; **7**:556
longitude **3**:179; **10**:750–751
loudspeakers **4**:247; **9**:703

Machines **6**:453–455
magnetic resonance imaging
    (MRI) **3**:224; **7**:*539*
magnetohydrodynamics
    (MHD) **6**:436
magnetometers **6**:446; **8**:638
Manhattan Project **4**:271
margarines **6**:412
marine exploration **6**:**441–444**
mass spectrometers **8**:567;
    9:657
medicine
    isotopes in **5**:*384*, 385
    See also surgery
metal detectors **6**:470
metallurgy **6**:**472–473**
microphones **4**:247; **9**:703
microprocessors **3**:231
    See also integrated circuits
microscopes **3**:*228*; **7**:*554*
    petrological **7**:491
microwave ovens **3**:230; **7**:*487*
mining **7**:**492–494**
    alluvial **7**:493–494
    auger **2**:140
    coal **2**:139–140
    copper **3**:165
    gold **4**:317; **6**:473; **7**:493,
        494
    open-pit bench **7**:493
    strip **2**:140; **7**:493
    surface (quarrying) **7**:493
    underground **7**:494
missiles
    aiming **3**:193

heat-seeking **5**:371
    and the Star Wars program
        5:398
motors **3**:224; **4**:247; **6**:434
multiple mirror telescopes
    (MMTs) **10**:735

Nagasaki **4**:271
Nautilus (submarine) **4**:271
neon signs **5**:374
Next Generation Space
    Telescope (NGST) **5**:347;
        10:735
nitroglycerin **4**:262–263
nuclear power **4**:271
nylon **8**:619–920

Ocean Drilling Project **5**:365
oscilloscopes, cathode-ray
    2:*106*, 107
ovens, microwave **3**:230; **7**:*487*

Pacemakers **1**:64
particle accelerators **7**:*538*;
    8:585–586; **10**:*725*, 727
pentaerythritol tetranitrate
    (PETN) **4**:263
periscopes **6**:407
pesticides, spraying **3**:233
PET scans **3**:*226*
phonographs **9**:705
photography **8**:**603–605**
    aerial **6**:440; **9**:668
    color **2**:147; **3**:197; **8**:*605*
    developing film **6**:407
    digital **8**:605
    film **5**:*337*
    flash **6**:428, *442*
    infrared **9**:668
    silver compounds used in
        9:691
    underwater **6**:*442*
    See also holography
photometers **2**:147
piezoelectricity **10**:765
pixels, LCD **6**:417
plasma, and MHD generators
    6:436
plastics **7**:501; **8**:**618–621**
power plants **3**:215, 233; **4**:259
    nuclear **4**:270; **8**:*626*
printing **2**:146–147
PTFE (polytetrafluoroethene)
    5:*337*; **8**:620
puddling furnace **5**:379

Quartz
    clocks/watches **10**:751

Volume numbers appear in **boldface type** followed by colons. Page numbers in **boldface type** refer to main articles and their illustrations. Page numbers in *italic type* refer to additional illustrations.

piezoelectricity **10**:765

Radar **1**:47; **9**:*659*
  and depth of glaciers **5**:361
  Doppler **3**:192, 193; **9**:*659*
  imaging tornadoes **10**:755
  police speed guns **3**:192, 193
  and remote sensing
    9:668–669
  and weather forecasts **3**:193;
    7:487, 521; **9**:*659*
radiometers **6**:446
radios **3**:229
radiotherapy **5**:*384*
reactors **4**:271, 289
recording studios **1**:14
refining **6**:473; **7**:551; **9**:*665*
remote sensing **9**:668–669
  satellites **5**:371; **9**:669
resistors **3**:230
reverberatory furnace **9**:693
rivets, blind **4**:263

Satellites **9**:680–681
  batteries in **1**:64
  Explorer probes **4**:260–261
  first **1**:35; **7**:516
  geostationary **9**:681
  infrared imaging from **5**:*370*,
    371; **10**:735
  and mapmaking **6**:*440*
  remote-sensing **5**:371; **9**:669
  solar panels **1**:64
  weather **2**:137; **5**:351, 371;
    7:*485*, 521, 547
SCADS **6**:444
scintillometers **8**:638
scuba equipment **6**:441–442,
  443; **7**:547
seawater
  drinking water from **6**:444
  magnesium from **6**:428–429
  ships powered using **6**:436
  table salt from **6**:428–429
seismographs **8**:638
seismometers **3**:206
semiconductors **9**:688
Semtex **4**:263
ships, powered using seawater
  6:436
Sidewinder missiles **5**:371
silencers **1**:13
smoke alarms **3**:230
solar panels **1**:64; **6**:446
sonar **3**:192; **6**:443; **9**:*705*;
  10:765
sound, used for prospecting
  8:638

sound chambers **1**:*13*
sound-level meters **1**:14
spacecraft, launched **3**:*174*, 175
space heaters **5**:*339*
space stations, and gravity
  5:328
spectrographs **9**:715
spectrometers **9**:*714*, 715
  mass **8**:567; **9**:657
  solar plasma **6**:446
spectroscopy **9**:714–715
spinnerets **10**:731
sprinkler systems **1**:29
Sputnik 1 (satellite) **4**:260
Star Wars program **5**:*398*
storage heaters, night **4**:245
Strategic Defense Initiative
  (SDI) **5**:*398*
submarines **4**:271; **6**:443–444;
  8:637
submersibles **6**:443–444; **7**:*548*,
  549
supercomputers, and weather
  forecasts **7**:486
superconductors **3**:175; **10**:739
supertwists **6**:417
surgery
  keyhole **4**:*267*
  laser **5**:398
synthetic fibers **10**:731

Teflon **5**:337; **8**:*619*, 620
telescopes **7**:557; **10**:732–735
  cosmic ray **3**:167
  first **1**:45; **7**:557
  Galilean **10**:733, *734*
  infrared **5**:371
  radio **9**:*658*; **10**:732, 734–735
  reflecting **7**:*557*; **10**:733
  refracting **10**:732–733, 734
  relector-refractor **10**:733
  See also Hubble Space
    Telescope
televisions **2**:106, *107*, 147;
  6:419
theodolites **6**:440; **10**:796
thermograms **5**:*338*, 371
thermometers **5**:341; **10**:739
thermoplastics **8**:620
thermosets **8**:620
tiles, silica **1**:17
tintypes **8**:604
TIROS 1 (satellite) **2**:137;
  7:*485*, 521
tokamaks **4**:289
torus **4**:289
trains
  aerodynamics **1**:15

  maglev **6**:*436*
transducers **4**:247
transformers **3**:215, 224
transistors **3**:230, 231; **9**:688
trinitrotoluene (TNT) **4**:263
triodes **3**:231
turbines **10**:*742*, 765

Ultrasound, uses **3**:193; **9**:*705*;
  10:*764*, 765
ultraviolet radiation, uses
  10:767
uranium, enriched **4**:295;
  5:384–385
uranium hexafluoride **4**:*295*;
  5:384–385

Vacuum flasks **5**:*339*
vacuum tubes **3**:231
Vanguard rockets **4**:260; **7**:516
virtual reality **9**:*708*

Watches, LCD **6**:417
weapons
  halogen gas **5**:*336*
  nuclear **4**:*271*
weather, satellites **2**:137; **5**:351,
  371; **7**:*485*, 521, 547
welding **4**:*293*; **8**:617
wind tunnels **1**:*17*
wiring, aluminum **1**:31

X rays **3**:177; **10**:798
  and barium sulfate **6**:469

Yamoto (water craft) **6**:436

PEOPLE

Adams, John Couch **7**:525
Agassiz, Louis **4**:307; **5**:364
Airy, George Biddel **7**:525
Alberti, Friedrich August von
  10:759
Aldrin, Edwin "Buzz" **1**:*35*, *37*,
  38; **4**:299; **6**:*422*; **7**:518
Alexander the Great **6**:443;
  7:546
Ampère, André Marie **3**:*214*,
  222; **6**:433–434
Amundsen, Roald **1**:34

The path of a comet.

Anderson, Carl **3**:226; **8**:585;
  10:727
Anning, Mary **4**:*282*
Appleton, Edward **5**:377
Archer, Frederick Scott **8**:604
Aristotle **8**:*610*
  and the elements **1**:55;
    2:122; **4**:275; **7**:513
  and gravity **5**:326
  and mechanics **6**:453; **7**:513
  model of the Universe **9**:708
  and optics **7**:556
  study of ocean life **7**:546
Armstrong, Neil **1**:35, *37*, 38;
  4:*298*; **7**:518
Arrhenius, Svante A. **1**:10;
  8:609
Augustus, Caesar **2**:86
Avogadro, Amedeo **8**:590

Bacon, Francis **2**:156
Baekeland, Leo H. **8**:619
Ballard, Robert **5**:359
Balmer, Johann **9**:715
Bardeen, John **3**:231
Barents, William **1**:41
Barton, Otis **6**:443–444
Bauer, Georg **7**:492
Bean, Alan **1**:38
Becher, Johann **2**:124
Becquerel, Antoine-Henri
  4:270; **8**:*612*; **9**:655
Beebe, Charles W. **6**:443–444;
  7:547
Berliner, Emile **9**:705
Bernard, Claude **1**:69
Bernoulli, Daniel **1**:18
Berzelius, Jöns Jakob **2**:104,
  117, 125; **8**:591
Bessemer, Henry **5**:379
Bjerknes, Vilhelm and Jacob
  7:485
Black, Joseph **5**:341
Bohr, Niels **3**:228; **8**:584;
  9:649; **10**:726

Boltwood, Bertram **4**:305
Boltzmann, Ludwig **5**:341
Borchgrevink, Carsten **1**:34
Bose, S.N. **8**:586
Boutan, Louis **6**:*442*
Boyle, Robert **2**:*122*, 123; **4**:293; **8**:608–609
Brahe, Sofie **1**:45, 46; **7**:528
Brahe, Tycho **1**:45, 46; **5**:326; **7**:527–528
Brattain, Walter **3**:231
Braun, Karl Ferdinand **2**:107
Braun, Wernher von **1**:36; **4**:260
Broglie, Louis-Victor-Pierre Raymond de **3**:227; **9**:649
Brongniart, Alexandre **4**:305
Bronsted, Johannes **1**:11
Brown, Robert **6**:415
Buchner, Eduard **2**:123
Buckland, William **4**:307
Bunsen, Robert **9**:715
Burnell, Jocelyn Bell **9**:647

Caesar, Julius **2**:86; **10**:749
Cannizzaro, Stanislao **8**:591
Carnot, Sadi **8**:611
Carothers, Wallace H. **8**:619, *620*; **10**:731
Carpenter, M. Scott **6**:*462*, 463, 465
Carson, Rachel **5**:336
Cayley, George **1**:18
Celsius, Anders **5**:341; **10**:739
Cernan, Eugene **4**:298
Chadwick, James **7**:526; **8**:584; **10**:726
Chaffee, Roger **1**:37
Chancourtois, Alexandre-Emile Beguyer de **8**:591
Charles, Jacques-Alexandre-César **4**:293; **8**:609
Chladni, Ernst **6**:478
Clairaut, Alexis **2**:149
Clavius, Christoph **2**:86; **10**:*749*
Collins, Michael **1**:*37*, 38; **4**:298
Columbus, Christopher **4**:302
Conrad, Charles "Pete" **1**:38; **4**:297, 299
Cook, James **1**:34; **6**:442
Cooper, L. Gordon **4**:297; **6**:463, 465
Copernicus, Nicolaus **1**:45; **3**:*169*, 198
Coriolis, Gaspard-Gustave de **1**:25; **10**:795

Corliss, Jack **5**:359
Cort, Henry **5**:379
Coulomb, Charles-Augustin de **4**:276; **6**:433
Courtois, Bernard **5**:335
Cousteau, Jacques-Yves **6**:441; **7**:547
Crick, Francis **1**:73
Crookes, William **2**:107; **3**:225
Cros, Charles **8**:605
Curie, Pierre and Marie **9**:*655*
Cutting, James Ambrose **8**:604
Cuvier, Georges **4**:305, 306

Daguerre, Louis **8**:603–604
Dalton, John **1**:*55–56*; **2**:124–125; **6**:451; **8**:583, 590
Daniell, John Frederic **1**:65
Darwin, Charles **4**:283; **6**:442
Davis, William Morris **5**:394
Davy, Humphry **1**:65, 78; **5**:335, 341; **6**:428
de Forest, Lee **3**:231
Democritus **1**:55; **2**:122; **6**:451; **8**:583, 613
Descartes, René **3**:169; **7**:557
Deville, Henri Saint-Claire **1**:30
Dewar, James **3**:175
Dionysius Exiguus **2**:87
Dioscorides **1**:27
Dirac, Paul **3**:226; **8**:584–585
Doppler, Christian Johann **3**:192
Ducos du Hauron, Louis **8**:605
Du Fay, Charles **3**:233
Du Pont, E.I. **4**:263

Earle, Sylvia A. **7**:*549*
Eastman, George **8**:604–605
Edison, Thomas Alva **3**:214; **6**:406; **8**:605; **9**:705
Eiffel, Gustave **3**:165
Einstein, Albert
    and Brownian motion **6**:415
    and electromagnetism **6**:434
    and energy **4**:248, 271; **6**:450
    general theory of relativity (theory of gravity) **4**:275–276; **5**:327, 328; **8**:612; **9**:*667*
    and light **3**:227; **9**:649

mass-energy equation **4**:271
    and the nuclear bomb **4**:271
    and the photoelectric effect **8**:602
    and space **10**:771
    special theory of relativity **8**:611–612; **9**:666–667, 709
Eisenhower, Dwight D. **6**:462–463; **7**:516
Empedocles **2**:122, 124
Eratosthenes **4**:302; **6**:439
Euclid of Alexandria **7**:556

Faraday, Michael
    and electromagnetism **3**:214, 219, 222, 223, 224; **6**:434; **8**:*611*
    isolation of magnesium **6**:428
Farenheit, Daniel **5**:341; **10**:739
Fermi, Enrico **4**:271; **7**:526, 539; **8**:626
Fischer, Emil **1**:69; **2**:95
Fizeau, A.H.L. **3**:193
Fleming, John Ambrose **3**:231
Forbes, Edward **6**:442
Foucault, Jean **6**:407
Franklin, Benjamin **3**:233; **5**:334; **6**:442; **8**:611
Franklin, Rosalind **1**:72–73
Fraunhofer, Joseph von **1**:47; **9**:*715*
Fresnel, Augustin **6**:405
Fujita, Ted **10**:755
Fuller, Buckminster **2**:98

Gagarin, Yuri **9**:674, *675*
Gahn, Johan **6**:437
Galilei, Galileo **8**:610
    astronomical observations **1**:45; **3**:169, 198; **7**:509, 525; **9**:708
    and gravity **4**:275; **5**:326; **7**:513, 527
    ideas about force and motion **4**:274; **7**:513
    and the pendulum **10**:749–750
    telescope **10**:733, *734*
Galle, John Gottfried **7**:525
Galvani, Luigi **3**:213–214
Gay-Lussac, Joseph **5**:335

Geiger, Hans **3**:166
Gell-Mann, Murray **8**:586, 613; **10**:727
Gibbs, John Willard **8**:609
Gilbert, William **3**:233; **6**:430, *433*
Glenn, John H. **6**:463, *465*
Goldstein, Eugen **2**:106–107
Gold, Thomas **9**:647
Graham, Thomas **4**:295
Grant, Ulysses S. **7**:521
Gregory XIII, Pope **2**:86, *87*; **10**:749
Griess, Johann Peter **3**:197
Grissom, Virgil "Gus" **1**:37; **4**:297; **6**:463, *464*, 465
Grove, William **1**:65
Gutenberg, Beno **3**:201, 203

Haber, Fritz **7**:531
Hadley, George **1**:25
Hahn, Otto **4**:270–271
Haise, Fred **1**:39
Hall, Charles Martin **1**:30
Halley, Edmond **2**:149; **7**:528
Harrison, John **6**:442; **10**:751
Hawkes, Graham **7**:549
Heaviside, Oliver **5**:377
Heisenberg, Werner Karl **9**:649
Hendricus, Jacobus **8**:608
Henry, Joseph **6**:434; **7**:485
Herodotus **3**:180
Héroult, Paul-Louis **1**:30
Herschel, Caroline **1**:46, 67; **3**:209
Herschel, John F.W. **8**:604
Herschel, William **1**:46–47, 67; **3**:209, 218–219; **5**:370; **10**:772
Hertz, Heinrich **3**:219–20; **9**:659
Hess, Victor **3**:166
Hewish, Antony **9**:647
Holland, John **6**:443
Holmes, Arthur **4**:305
Hooke, Robert **3**:210; **7**:557; **10**:750
Huangdi, *emperor of China* **2**:87
Hubble, Edwin **3**:169; **4**:291; **10**:769
Humboldt, Alexander von **4**:302; **7**:485
Hutton, James **5**:364, 394; **9**:672
Huygens, Christiaan **6**:405; **7**:557; **9**:683; **10**:733, *750*

Volume numbers appear in **boldface type** followed by colons. Page numbers in **boldface type** refer to main articles and their illustrations. Page numbers in *italic type* refer to additional illustrations.

Hyatt, John W. **8:**619

Jeans, James **7:**557
Johanson, Don **4:**283
Joule, James P. **3:**174; **4:***248*;
    5:*340*, 341; **8:**611; **10:**743

Kelvin, Lord *See* Thomson,
    William
Kennedy, John F. **1:**35; **6:**422;
    7:518
Kennelly, Arthur **5:**377
Kepler, Johannes **1:**45, 46;
    3:169; **5:**326; **7:**527–528;
    9:717
Kilby, Jack **3:**231
Kirchoff, Robert **9:**715
Krebs, Hans **1:***71*
Kremer, Gerhard *See*
    Mercator, Gerardus

Lanchester, Frederick **1:**18
Land, Edwin L. **2:**146
Laplace, Pierre-Simon **3:**198
Lavoisier, Antoine **1:**10, 30;
    2:*123*–124; **5:**341; **6:**451
Lavoisier, Marie **1:**10, 30;
    2:123–124; **6:**451
Leakey, Louis, Mary and
    Richard **1:**22
Leavitt, Henrietta **1:***47*
Leclanché, Georges **1:**65
Lehmann, Otto **6:**416
Lemaître, Georges **3:**169
Leonardo da Vinci **1:**18; **8:**603
Leonov, Alexei **9:**675
Lepaute, Nicole-Reine **2:**149
le Roy, Pierre **10:**751
Le Verrier, Urbain-Jean-
    Joseph **7:**525
Lewis, Gilbert Newton **1:**11
Libby, Willard **5:***385*; **9:**657
Lipmann, Fritz **1:***71*
Lippershey, Hans **10:**734
Lockyer, Norman **5:**342
London, Fritz **6:**415
Lovell, James **1:**38–39; **4:**299
Lowry, Thomas **1:**11
Lumière, Auguste-Marie and
    Louis-Jean **8:**605
Lyell, Charles **4:**304, 307

McDivitt, James **4:**297
Maddox, Richard Leach **8:**604
Magellan, Ferdinand **7:**544
Marconi, Guglielmo **5:**377;
    9:659
Maricourt, Pierre de **6:**432–433

Marshall, James **4:**317; **7:**494
Marsili, Luigi **6:**442
Mary the Jewess **2:**122
Maury, Matthew Fontaine
    7:546
Maxwell, James Clerk
    and color photography **8:**605
    and electromagnetism
        3:214–215, 219; **4:**276;
        6:434; **7:**557; **8:**611
    and heat **5:**341
Meitner, Lise **4:**271
Mendeleyev, Dmitri **1:**57;
    2:125; **8:**591–594, 626
Mercator, Gerardus (Gerhard
    Kremer) **4:**302, 303; **6:**439,
    440
Michelson, Albert **9:**709
Milankovitch, Milutin **5:**364–365
Miller, Stanley **1:**72
Millikan, Robert **3:**227
Mohammed **2:**87
Mohorovicic, Andrija **3:**201,
    202
Mohs, Friedrich **4:**301; **7:**491
Molina, Mario José **5:**337
Morley, Edward **9:**709
Moseley, Henry **8:**593
Mossain, Henri **5:**336
Müller, Franz **6:***471*
Müller, Paul **5:**336
Murchison, Roderick **2:**89;
    3:188; **8:**598, *599*; **9:**689
Murdock, William **2:**139

Newlands, John **8:**591
Newton, Isaac **7:**528; **8:**609
    and the apple **7:***529*
    and gravity **1:**46; **4:**251,
        274–275; **5:***326*–327;
        7:513, 528–529; **9:**708
    laws of motion **2:**114, 115;
        4:274, 277; **5:**327;
        6:452–453; **7:**504,
        512–513
    and light **2:**144; **6:**405; **7:***528*,
        529; **9:**660, 661, 715
    model of tides **10:**746–747
    telescope **7:***557*; **10:**734
Niepce, Joseph-Nicéphore and
    Claude **8:**603
Noah **4:**272
Northrop, John **2:**123
Noyce, Robert **3:**231

Orsted, Hans Christian **1:**30;
    3:214, 222; **4:**276; **6:**433
Ostwald, Wilhelm **8:**608, 609

Pascal, Blaise **1:***25*
Pauling, Linus **7:***502*
Pearson, Allen **10:**755
Perkin, William **3:**196–197
Peter the Pilgrim **6:**432 433
Phips, William **6:**443
Piazzi, Giuseppe **1:**43
Piccard, August **6:**444
Piccard, Jacques **6:**444
Planck, Max **7:**557; **9:**649
Plato **7:**556
Plücker, Julius **2:**106
Powell, John Wesley **2:**90;
    10:768
Prandtl, Ludwig **1:**17, 18
Priestley, Joseph **2:**123, 124;
    6:458, 459; **7:**530; **8:***573*
Proust, Joseph-Louis **1:**55
Ptolemy, Claudius **1:***45*; **2:**152;
    3:*168*–169; **4:***302*
    mapmaking **6:**439

Rayleigh, Lord **7:**557
Richter, Charles **3:**206
Ritter, Johann Wilhelm **3:**219
Romer, Ole **6:**407
Röntgen, William **3:**177, 221;
    10:798
Roosevelt, Franklin D. **4:**271
Rowland, F. Sherwood **5:**337
Rutherford, Daniel **7:**530
Rutherford, Ernest **2:**107
    and atomic change **4:**270
    and the neutron **7:**539; **8:**584
    nuclear atom model **1:**57;
        3:227–228; **7:**538–539;
        8:584, 612; **10:**726
    and radioactivity **4:**307;
        9:655

Scheele, Carl **2:**123; **5:**335;
    6:437; **7:**530
Schirra, Walter M., Jr. **6:**463,
    465
Schmidt, Bernhard **10:**733
Schmidt, Maarten **9:**651
Schönbein, Christian **1:**65
Schrödinger, Erwin **3:**228;
    9:649
Scott, David **4:**298
Scott, Robert **1:**34
Sedgwick, Adam **2:**89; **3:**188;
    4:306
Segrè, Emilio **5:**336

Sertürner, Friedrich **1:**27
Shackleton, Ernest **1:**34
Shepard, Alan B. **1:**35; **6:**463,
    464, 465; **7:**518
Shockley, William **3:***231*
Slayton, Donald K. **6:**463
Smith, William **4:***305*, 306;
    8:588
Snell, Willebrord **7:**557
Sorensen, Soren **1:**11
Sosigenes **2:**86
Spitzer, Lyman **5:**347
Stafford, Thomas **4:**298
Stahl, Georg Ernst **2:**124;
    8:573
Starr, J.W. **6:**406
Strabo **4:**302
Strassmann, Fritz **4:**270–271
Sturgeon, William **3:**224;
    6:434
Suess, Eduard **5:**373
Sumner, James **1:**71; **2:**123
Sutter, James Augustus **4:**317
Sutter, John **7:**494
Svedberg, Theodor **1:**69
Swan, Joseph Wilson **3:**214;
    6:406
Swigert, John **1:**38–39

Talbot, William Henry Fox
    8:604
Tereshkova, Valentina **9:**674,
    675
Tesla, Nikolai **3:**224
Thales of Miletus **2:**121; **3:**233
Thompson, Benjamin (Count
    Rumford) **5:**341
Thomson, J.J. **1:**56; **2:**107;
    3:215, *225*–227; **7:**538;
    8:584, 612; **10:**725
Thomson, William (Lord
    Kelvin) **3:**174; **4:***305*; **5:**341;
    10:*743*
Tombaugh, Clyde **8:***625*
Torricelli, Evangelista **1:**24

Urey, Harold **1:**72

Van Allen, James **4:**260
Van de Graaff, Robert **3:**233
Verne, Jules **6:**441
Vinci, Leonardo da **1:**18; **8:**603

*The flow of air around an
airfoil, such as an
airplane wing.*

Vine, Allyn **6:**444
Volta, Alessandro **1:**65; **3:**214, 215; **6:**433

Waals, Johannes van der **7:**502
Walcott, Charles Doolittle **2:**89
Walsh, Don **6:**444
Watson, James **1:**73
Wegener, Alfred **2:**156; **4:**318; **8:**582, 622
Wells, H. G. **10:**752, *753*
White, Edward **1:**37; **4:**297, 298, *299*
Wien, Wilhelm **9:**646
Winkler, Clemens Alexander **8:**594
Wöhler, Friedrich **1:**30, 69
Wright, Wilbur and Orville **1:**18
Wyville, Charles **6:**442–443

Young, John **4:**297, 298
Young, Thomas **6:***405*–406; **7:**557

Zweig, George **8:**586, 613; **10:**727

PLACES

Aden, Gulf of **1:**19
Adriatic Sea **6:**456
Africa **1:19–22; 8:**622
    grasslands **5:**324, *325*
    joined to South America
    rift valleys **5:**393, 394–395
Ahaggar Mountains **1:**20
Alaska
    earthquakes **3:**207
    oil pipeline **8:**597
    permafrost **8:**596, *597*
Albert, Lake **1:**22
Aleutian Islands **7:**544; **8:**577
Allegheny Mountains **8:**588
Alps **1:**63; **2:**113; **4:**257
Amazon Basin **9:**706; **10:**761
Amazon River **3:**180; **9:**670,
Andes Mountains **5:**395; **8:**577, 623; **9:**706
Antarctica **1:32–34; 3:**185; **8:***628*

glaciers **4:**310, 311
hole in the ozone layer over **1:***33*; **8:**575
meteorites on **6:**478
permafrost **8:**596
tundra **10:**762
Antarctic Ocean **7:**540
Antler Highlands **8:**589
Appalachian Mountains **7:**533, 535; **8:**598; **10:**740
Arabian peninsula **2:**156
Aral Sea **5:**372–373
Arctic Ocean **1:40–41**
Arecibo, radio telescope **10:**734–735
Argentina **9:**707
Arizona, Meteor Crater **6:***477*
Asia **7:**507; **6:***438*
Assal, Lake **1:**20
Athabasca glacier **4:***311*
Atlantic Ocean **1:48–50**
    formation **1:**48–49; **2:**102, 141, 157
    Gulf Stream **1:**50; **2:**131; **5:**334; **6:**442; **7:**542
Atlas Mountains **1:**20
Australasia **1:60–61; 2:**156; **7:**544
Australia **1:**60–61; **7:**544
    Great Artesian Basin **5:**331–332
    tornadoes **10:**755
Axial Volcano **3:**171
Ayer's Rock **3:***185*
Azores **1:**48
Azov, Sea of **5:***372*, 373

Baikal, Lake **5:**392
Bangladesh **4:**273; **5:**351
Barberton Mountains **8:**635
Bass Strait **1:**61
Bechun Cave, Utah **2:**111
Bengal, Bay of **5:**351; **7:***507*
Bering Strait **2:**113; **9:**652
Bhopal, chemical disaster **8:**601
Black Forest **4:**280
Black Hills, South Dakota **2:**110
Black Sea **5:***372*, 373
Blanc, Mont **4:**257
Bosporus Strait **5:**373
Brazil **9:**707

British Isles **5:**380
Bryce Canyon, Utah **2:***112*

Calama **9:**663
California **7:**535
    earthquakes **7:**534
    Gold Rush (1849) **4:**317; **7:**494; **8:**565
Cameroon Highlands **1:**19
Canada
    ice ages **5:***365*
    permafrost **8:**596
Caribbean Sea **2:102–103**
Carlsbad Caverns **2:**110; **5:***331*
Caroline Islands **7:**545
Cascade Range **7:**515, 535; **8:**577
Caspian Sea **5:**372
Central America, climate **7:**535
Chad, Lake **1:**22
Chernobyl **4:**271; **9:***654*
Cherrapunji **7:***507*; **9:**663
Chesapeake Bay **2:**141
Chichén Itzá **4:**251
Chicxulub, meteorite impact **4:***265*
Chile, earthquake **3:**207
China, floods **4:**273
Chiquicamata, Chile **3:**165
Colorado Plateau **7:**533–534
Colorado River **2:**90–91, 129; **7:**534; **10:**740
Columbia Plateau **5:**367
Concepción **10:**745
Congo River **1:**21
Cottonwood caves, New Mexico **2:**110
Crater Lake **3:**170; **5:**393
Crater Mound **3:**171
Crete **2:**129; **10:**745
Cuba **2:**102
Cyprus **3:**164

Dachstein **2:**110
Dead Sea **5:**373
Death Valley, California **4:***255*; **7:**533
Dominica **2:**103
Drakensberg Mountains **1:**19

Edward, Lake **1:**22
Eisreisenwelt **2:**110
El Chinchonal **2:**133

Eniwetok Atoll **4:**289
Erie, Lake **5:***392*
Ethiopia, lakes **5:***393*
Ethiopian Highlands **1:**19
Euphrates River **4:**272
Eurasia **4:256–257**
Everest, Mount **3:**200; **4:**257; **7:**514

Fiji islands **7:**544
Fingal's Cave **2:**111
Fuji, Mount **7:**514; **10:**780
Fundy, Bay of **10:**747

Galilee, Sea of **5:**393
Galveston Island **7:**521
Ganges River **3:**180
    delta **3:**181; **4:**273
    geography **4:302–303**
Gibraltar, Straits of **6:**456
Gobi Desert **3:**184
Grand Banks **1:**49; **2:**158
Grand Canyon **2:**90–91, 129; **7:**533–534; **10:***768*, 774
Great Artesian Basin **5:**331–332
Great Barrier Reef **5:**395
Great Dividing Range **1:**60
Greater Antilles **2:**102
Great Lakes **2:**113, 131; **5:***392*; **9:**653
    Fata Morgana mirage **7:**495
Great Nevada Basin **7:**535
Great Plains **3:**195; **4:**255; **5:***332*; **7:**535
Great Rift Valley **1:**19, 21; **4:**266, 285; **8:**623
Great Salt Lake **5:**393
Greenland **3:**185, 189; **4:**310, 311; **5:**381; **8:**635

Haicheng, earthquake **3:**207
Hawaiian Islands **3:**201; **7:**515, 545; **8:**577
    volcanoes **2:**110; **3:**170; **10:**781
Hell's Canyon **2:**91
Hercynian Mountains **8:**589
Himalaya Mountains **2:**113; **3:**200; **4:**267, 318
Hiroshima **4:***271*
Honshu **10:**745
Huascaran, Mount **1:**63
Huron, Lake **5:***392*

Iceland **1:**48; **4:***256*, 311
India **5:**369
Indian Ocean **5:368–369**

Volume numbers appear in **boldface type** followed by colons. Page numbers in **boldface type** refer to main articles and their illustrations. Page numbers in *italic type* refer to additional illustrations.

Ireland, cliffs **2**:128, 129
Irian Barat **1**:60
Italy, floods **4**:273

Jamaica **2**:102
Japan **4**:273; **7**:558; **8**:577
Johnstown, Pennsylvania, flood
    4:273

Kara Strait **1**:41
Kauai **10**:789
Kazumura Cave **2**:110
Kea, Mount **10**:735
Kenya **1**:22; **5**:393
Kenya, Mount **1**:19
Kerch Strait **5**:373
Kilauea volcano **2**:110; **3**:170
Kilimanjaro, Mount **1**:19, 21
Kivu, Lake **1**:22
Klonk **3**:188
Kobe, earthquake **3**:207
Koobi Fara **1**:22
Kosciusko, Mount **1**:61; **7**:544
Krakatoa, Mount **4**:257;
    10:744

Labrador Sea **1**:50
Laccadive Islands **5**:369
Laetoli **4**:283–284
Lena River **1**:41
Lesser Antilles **2**:102
Lituya Bay **10**:745
Love Canal **10**:757
Lubang Nasib Bagus **2**:108

Mackenzie River **1**:41
McKinley, Mount **1**:62; **7**:533
Madagascar **5**:368
Malawi, Lake **1**:22
Maldive Islands **5**:369
Marianas **7**:545
Marmara, Sea of **5**:372, 373;
    6:456
Marshall Islands **7**:545
Matterhorn **4**:254; **7**:514
Mauna Kea **7**:515
Mauna Loa **3**:170
Mazama, Mount **3**:170
Mead, Lake **2**:91
Mediterranean Sea **1**:50;
    2:158; **5**:372; **6**:456
    in the Cenozoic **2**:113
    formation **2**:157; **10**:741
Mekong delta **3**:*181*
Melanesia **7**:544–545; **8**:577
Messina, Strait of **7**:495
Mexico City, earthquake **3**:*205*,
    207

Mexico, Gulf of **10**:747
Michigan, Lake **5**:*392*
Micronesia **7**:545; **8**:577
Mississippi River **9**:670, 687
    delta **3**:180, *181*
    floods **4**:272, 273
Missoula, Lake **2**:113
Montserrat **2**:103
Moorea **7**:*545*
Murray River **1**:61
Myanmar, oil wells **7**:550

Nagasaki **4**:271
Nakuru, Lake **1**:21
Navan **4**:267
Nevado de Ruiz, Mount
    10:781
New Caledonia **7**:544
New Guinea **1**:60, 61; **7**:544
New Hebrides **7**:544
New Madrid, Missouri,
    earthquake **3**:207
New Zealand **2**:*131*; **5**:381;
    7:544, 545
Niger River **1**:21
Nile River **1**:21; **4**:272, 273;
    9:670
    delta **3**:180, *181*
North America **7**:533–535
    during the Cambrian **2**:*89*;
    8:581
    during the Silurian **9**:689
    ice ages **5**:*365*; **9**:*653*
    time zones **10**:*751*
North American Cordillera
    7:533, 535
Norway **2**:128, 129; **10**:*736*
Nyasa, Lake **5**:393

Oceania **1**:60; **7**:544–545
    See also Australasia
Ohio River, floodplains **4**:272
Olduvai Gorge **1**:22
Ontario, Lake **5**:*392*
Oregon **5**:367; **7**:535
Ouachita Mountains **8**:588

Pacific Ocean **8**:576–577
    El Niño and La Niña
    3:236–238; **8**:*576*, 577
    hydrothermal vents **5**:359
    Ring of Fire **3**:205; **4**:267;
    8:623
    tidal waves **10**:744
    trenches **7**:*541*; **8**:576; **9**:707
    See also Oceania
Painted Desert **10**:759
Panama **2**:156; **9**:706

Papua New Guinea **1**:*60*
Patagonian Desert **3**:184
Peru, rain forest destruction
    4:279
Philippines, floods **4**:273
Pinatubo, Mount **4**:257
Polynesia **7**:*545*; **8**:577
Puerto Rico **2**:102

Red Sea **1**:19
Rocky Mountains **7**:535;
    8:589; **10**:740
    Chinook winds **10**:797
    coal beds **2**:138
    fossils **4**:285
Rub al Khali **3**:185
Russia **5**:324; **8**:596; **10**:757

Sacramento, Gold Rush
    (1849) **4**:317; **7**:494; **8**:565
Sahara Desert **1**:22; **3**:184,
    185; **5**:329
St. Helens, Mount **2**:133;
    3:*170*; **7**:515
San Francisco **3**:204–205, 207;
    4:267; **7**:494
Santa Ana Mountains **10**:797
Sarawak, caves **2**:108, 109
Sargasso Sea **1**:49
Seychelles **5**:368; **10**:*760*
Siberia, meteorite impact
    6:478
Sierra Nevada (United States)
    7:535
Snake River **2**:91
Snake River Plateau **2**:113
Society Islands **7**:*545*
Solomon Islands **7**:544
South Africa, diamonds **4**:301
South America **5**:324;
    9:706–707
    joined to Africa **8**:622
Southern Ocean **7**:540
Sri Lanka **5**:368, 380
Stonehenge **1**:44
Sudan, floods **4**:273
Sumatra **5**:369
Superior, Lake **5**:*392*
Suwarrow **5**:381

Table Mountain **7**:514
Tahiti **7**:*545*
Tahoe, Lake **5**:393
Tambora, Mount **2**:133; **4**:257
Tanganyika, Lake **1**:21–22;
    5:393
Tanzania **1**:22; **5**:393
Tavurvur, Mount **1**:*60*
Three Mile Island **4**:271
Tibesti Mountains **1**:20
Titicaca, Lake **9**:707
Toubkal, Jebel **1**:20
Transantarctic Mountains **1**:33
Trinidad and Tobago **2**:102
Tunguska, Siberia **2**:149
Turkey, earthquakes **3**:207
Tyrrhenian Sea **6**:456

United States
    earthquakes **3**:*207*
    floods **4**:272–273
    ice ages **5**:*365*
    tornadoes **10**:755
Ural Mountains **4**:257; **8**:599
Uruguay **9**:707

Venezuela, floods **4**:273
Victoria, Lake **1**:21
Virgin Islands **2**:102

Washington, basalts **5**:367
Weddell Sea **1**:50
Western Australian Shield **1**:60
West Indies **2**:102

Yellowstone National Park
    2:113; **4**:309; **5**:331
Yosemite National Park **4**:254
Yosemite valley **5**:367
Yucatán peninsula, meteorite
    impact **3**:173; **4**:*265*; **6**:476
Yukon River **9**:*671*

Zaire River **1**:21
Zambezi River **1**:21

The magnetic field around a bar magnet.

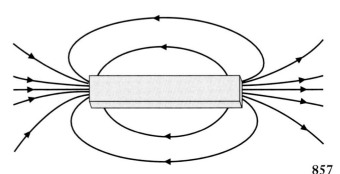

General Index

Abrasion **5**:363
absolute zero **3**:174; **4**:293; **5**:339–340; **10**:743
acceleration
    and force **4**:277; **6**:453; **7**:512
    due to gravity **5**:327–328
accumulators (rechargeable batteries) **1**:65; **3**:216
acetic acid **1**:*10*; **2**:119–120
acid rain **1**:75; **5**:357; **7**:531; **8**:631; **9**:693
    and coal **2**:140
acids and bases **1**:**10–11**; **5**:355; **9**:676–677
acoustics **1**:**12–14**; **9**:705
    See also sound
acrylic fibers **10**:731
acrylic paints **8**:579
actinides **8**:595
actinium **8**:595
Adams, John Couch **7**:525
Aden, Gulf of **1**:19
adenine **1**:71–72
adenosine triphosphate (ATP) **1**:71
Adriatic Sea **6**:456
aerobraking **6**:425
aerodynamics **1**:**15–18**
aerogel **8**:*633*
aeronautics, and NASA **7**:519
aerospace planes **7**:519
Africa **1**:**19–22**
    grasslands **5**:324, *325*
    joined to South America **8**:622
    rift valleys **5**:393, 394–395
Agassiz, Louis **4**:307; **5**:364
Agena (space vehicle) **4**:297, 298
Agent Orange **5**:336
Ahaggar Mountains **1**:20
AIDS (acquired immune deficiency syndrome) **1**:73
air
    compressed **6**:441
    density **1**:25
airbags, automobile **4**:263
air conditioning **5**:349
air currents *See* jet streams
air distillation **8**:573
airfoils **1**:18

airplanes
    aerodynamics **1**:15, *16–17*
    aerospace planes **7**:519
    aluminum **1**:31
    contrails **2**:137
    flight **1**:*16–17*, *18*
    motion **7**:*513*
    noise **1**:14
    pressurised cabins **1**:24
    use of radar **7**:487
    white trails made by **1**:*52*
air (atmospheric) pressure **1**:**23–25**, 52; **7**:485
    and monsoons **7**:506
air resistance (drag) **1**:15
airships **3**:183; **5**:*354*
air showers **3**:167
Airy, George Biddel **7**:525
Alaska
    earthquakes **3**:207
    oil pipeline **8**:597
    permafrost **8**:596, *597*
albedo **2**:130
Alberti, Friedrich August von **10**:759
Albert, Lake **1**:22
albumen **9**:645
alchemists **2**:*121*, 122–123
aldehyde groups **2**:95
aldoses **2**:95
Aldrin, Edwin "Buzz" **1**:*35*, *37*, *38*; **4**:299; **6**:*422*; **7**:518
Aleutian Islands **7**:544; **8**:577
Alexander the Great **6**:443; **7**:546
alizarin **3**:197
alkali metals **6**:468–469
alkaline earth metals **6**:469
alkaloids **1**:**26–27**
alkanes, isomers of **5**:382
alkenes **5**:352, 353
alkynes **5**:352, 353
Allegheny Mountains **8**:588
alloys **1**:**28–29**; **6**:472; **8**:607
    aluminum **6**:429
    copper **3**:164, 165
    gold **4**:317

hydrogen atoms in **3**:191
made in space **9**:711
magnesium **6**:428, 429
magnetism **6**:435
manganese **6**:437
silver **9**:691
    See also brass; bronze; iron and steel
alluvial fans **4**:253; **9**:671
alnico **6**:435
Alpha Centauri system **1**:66
alpha helix **9**:644
alpha particles **1**:57; **5**:385; **7**:526; **9**:654–655; **10**:726
Alps **1**:63; **2**:113; **4**:257; **10**:775
Altair **2**:155
alternating current (AC) **3**:213
altitude **1**:24, 52–53; **2**:*131*; **4**:278
aluminum **1**:**30–31**; **8**:564
    alloys **6**:429
    recycling **1**:*31*; **8**:565
aluminum bronze **1**:29; **3**:165
aluminum hydroxide **1**:31
aluminum oxide **1**:*30*, 31
aluminum silicate **1**:30
aluminum sulfate **1**:31
alums **1**:30
Alvin (submersible) **5**:359; **6**:444
amalgamation, gold **4**:317
amalgams **1**:*29*
Amazon Basin **9**:706; **10**:761
Amazon River **3**:180; **9**:670, 706
amazon stone **7**:*490*
amber **4**:285, 300
ambrotyping **8**:604
amethysts **4**:300, 301; **9**:650
amine group **1**:68, 69
amino acids **1**:68, 69; **8**:567, *633*; **9**:*644, 645*
ammonia **1**:10, 11; **5**:355; **7**:*503*, 531
    industrial production **2**:105; **5**:355; **7**:531

reaction with hydrochloric acid **1**:11
ammonites **3**:172, 173; **4**:*284, 285*; **5**:391; **6**:467
ammonium chloride **1**:11
ammonium cyanate **1**:69
ammonium ions **1**:11; **5**:375; **7**:503
ammonoids **10**:759
Ampère, André Marie **3**:*214*, 222; **6**:433–434
amperes (amps) **3**:214
amphibians **3**:189; **7**:497; **8**:581, 589, 599
amphiboles **9**:673
Amundsen, Roald **1**:34
Anaximenes **2**:121–122
Anderson, Carl **3**:226; **8**:585; **10**:727
andesite magma **6**:426, 427; **8**:623
Andes Mountains **5**:395; **8**:577, 623; **9**:706
Andromeda Galaxy **2**:155
Andromedids **6**:477
anechoic chambers **1**:14
anemometers **10**:796
aneroid cells **1**:24
anesthetics **1**:26, 27
angina, treatment **4**:263
ANGUS (underwater camera sled) **5**:359
anhydrite **8**:598–599
anions **5**:374; **9**:646
ankylosaurs **3**:173
Anning, Mary **4**:*282*
Antarctica **1**:**32–34**; **3**:185; **8**:*628*
    glaciers **4**:310, 311
    hole in the ozone layer over **1**:*33*; **8**:575
    meteorites on **6**:478
    permafrost **8**:596
    tundra **10**:762
Antarctic Circumpolar Current **1**:50; **8**:577
Antarctic Ocean **7**:540
Antarctic Treaty **1**:34; **8**:629
anthracene **3**:197
anthracite **2**:98, 140
anthraquinone **3**:197
antibodies **9**:645

Volume numbers appear in **boldface type** followed by colons. Page numbers in **boldface type** refer to main articles and their illustrations. Page numbers in *italic type* refer to additional illustrations.

anticlines **7**:515
anticline traps **7**:*522*
anticyclones **10**:790
antimatter **3**:226; **8**:584–585, 586; **10**:727
antimony **6**:471
antiquarks **8**:586
Antler Highlands **8**:589
apeiron **2**:121
Apollo missions **1**:35–39; **4**:275; **6**:422–423; **7**:510, 511, 518
IMPs **4**:261
Appalachian Mountains **7**:533, 535; **8**:598; **10**:740
Appleton, Edward **5**:377
Appleton layer **5**:377
aqualungs **6**:441
aqua regia **4**:316
aquifers **5**:*330*, 331–332, 333, 357; **10**:785
Arabian peninsula **2**:156
Aral Sea **5**:372–373
archaeobacteria **5**:359
Archaeopteryx **4**:*264*
Archean eon **8**:634
Archer, Frederick Scott **8**:604
arches, sea **4**:254
Archimedes's screw **6**:455
Arctic Ocean **1**:40–41
Arctic region **7**:535; **8**:628, 629; **10**:762
hole in the ozone layer over **8**:575
Arecibo, radio telescope **10**:734–735
argenite **9**:690
Argentina **9**:707
argon **4**:*295*
Ariel (moon) **10**:*773*
Aristotle **8**:*610*
and the elements **1**:55; **2**:122; **4**:275; **7**:513
and gravity **5**:326
and mechanics **6**:453; **7**:513
model of the Universe **9**:708
and optics **7**:556
study of ocean life **7**:546
Arizona, Meteor Crater **6**:*477*
Armstrong, Neil **1**:35, *37*, 38; **4**:298; **7**:518
aromatic compounds **5**:353, 382–383; **8**:601
Arrhenius, Svante A. **1**:10; **8**:609
arroyos **9**:670; **10**:775
arsenic **6**:471
Asia **7**:507
map **6**:*438*

asphalt **8**:*587*
Assal, Lake **1**:20
astatine **3**:235; **5**:335, 336; **6**:471
asteroids **1**:42–43; **2**:148; **3**:171; **6**:477; **9**:696, 698
astronauts
and centrifugal forces **2**:*114*, 115
and gravity **5**:328; **10**:791
women **6**:463
astronomical units (AUs) **9**:697
astronomy **1**:44–47
See also constellations; telescopes
Atacama Trench **9**:707
ATDA **4**:298
Athabasca glacier **4**:*311*
Atlantic Ocean **1**:48–50
formation **1**:48–49; **2**:102, 141, 157
Gulf Stream **1**:50; **2**:131; **5**:*334*; **6**:442; **7**:542
See also Mid-Atlantic Ridge
Atlantis (space shuttle) **7**:*519*; **9**:713
Atlas Mountains **1**:20
Atlas rockets **4**:299; **6**:*462*, 464
atmosphere **1**:51–54; **2**:134; **3**:199, 220
and auroras **1**:59
gases **1**:52, 59; **2**:100; **7**:530
humidity **5**:348–349
layers **1**:*52*–54; **5**:386
past composition **1**:54; **4**:315
See also clouds; ozone layer; stratosphere; winds
Atmospheric Explorers **4**:261
atmospheric pressure *See* air (atmospheric) pressure
atolls **5**:*380*, 381
atomic mass **1**:56–57
atomic mass number
and isotopes **5**:384
See also atomic weight
atomic mass units
and isotopes **5**:384
See also atomic weight
atomic number **1**:56; **5**:384; **8**:584, 593; **9**:646
atomic weight **2**:125; **8**:591, 593
See also atomic mass number
atoms **1**:55–57; **2**:150; **3**:234–235
and the Big Bang **10**:770
and color **2**:145
and Democritus **1**:55; **2**:122; **6**:451; **8**:583

electrons in **1**:*56*; **2**:107, 145; **3**:227–228, 234–235; **5**:396–397; **6**:418; **8**:*583*, 584
nucleus *See* nucleus, atomic
shells **1**:57; **3**:234–235; **5**:396–397; **8**:584
structure *See* subatomic structure
See also fission, nuclear; fusion, nuclear
ATP (adenosine triphosphate) **1**:71
augers **6**:455
Augustus, Caesar **2**:86
Aurora 7 (spacecraft) **6**:465
auroras **1**:54, **58**–**59**; **6**:431, 435; **8**:617
AUs (astronomical units) **9**:697
Australasia **1**:60–61; **2**:156; **7**:544
Australia **1**:60–61; **7**:544
Great Artesian Basin **5**:331–332
tornadoes **10**:755
australopithecines **4**:283–284
automobiles
aerodynamics **1**:16, *17*, 18
airbags **4**:263
batteries **1**:*65*
catalytic converters **2**:*105*; **4**:*313*
cornering **2**:*115*
fuel cells **5**:355
ignition **6**:436
jacks **6**:*453*
spraying **3**:233
starter motor **6**:436
avalanches **1**:62–63
Avogadro, Amedeo **8**:590
Avogadro's hypothesis **8**:590–591
Axial Volcano **3**:171
Ayer's Rock **3**:*185*
azo dyes **3**:197
Azores **1**:48
azote **2**:124
Azov, Sea of **5**:*372*, 373

Babylonians, calendar **2**:85
Bacon, Francis **2**:156
Bacon, Roger **7**:556–557

bacteria
and the nitrogen cycle **7**:531
sulfur **8**:577
badlands **4**:255
Baekeland, Leo H. **8**:619
Baikal, Lake **5**:392, 393
Bakelite **8**:619
baking soda **6**:468–469
Ballard, Robert **5**:359
balloons, weather **7**:*484*; **10**:796
Balmer, Johann **9**:715
Bangladesh **4**:273; **5**:351
Barberton Mountains **8**:635
barcode readers **5**:398
Bardeen, John **3**:231
Barents, William **1**:41
barite **6**:419
See barium sulfate
barium **6**:469
barium sulfate (barite) **6**:419, 469; **8**:564
barographs **1**:*23*, 24
barometers **1**:24, 25; **5**:349; **6**:458; **7**:485
bars, in rivers **9**:671, 679
Barton, Otis **6**:443–444
basalt **5**:366, 367; **6**:426–427; **7**:490; **9**:672
island **5**:380, 381
base bullion **9**:693
bases **1**:10, 11
bases, DNA **1**:71–72
bases *See* acids and bases
Bass Strait **1**:61
batholiths **5**:367; **6**:427
bathyscaphes **6**:444
bathyspheres **6**:443–444; **7**:547
batteries **1**:64–65; **3**:214, *215*; **10**:742–743
long-life (alkaline) **1**:65
rechargeable **1**:65; **3**:216
zinc–carbon (dry cells) **1**:64–65
Bauer, Georg **7**:492
bauxite **1**:30, 31
beaches, sandy **9**:679; **10**:787
Bean, Alan **1**:38
Beaufort scale **10**:796

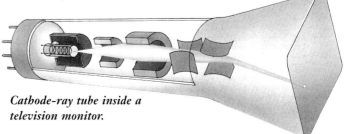

Cathode-ray tube inside a television monitor.

Becher, Johann 2:124
Bechun Cave, Utah 2:111
Becquerel, Antoine-Henri 4:270; 8:612; 9:655
Beebe, Charles W. 6:443–444; 7:547
belemnites 3:172, 173; 5:391
bends, the 6:442
Bengal, Bay of 5:351; 7:507
benzene 2:139; 5:353; 8:601
    and isomers 5:382–383
Bering Strait 2:113; 9:652
Berliner, Emile 9:705
berms 2:143
Bernard, Claude 1:69
Bernoulli, Daniel 1:18
beryllium 6:469
beryllium dichloride 7:503
Berzelius, Jöns Jakob 2:104, 117, 125; 8:591
Bessemer, Henry 5:379
beta decay 5:385; 7:526; 9:655
Betelgeuse 2:155
Bhopal, chemical disaster 8:601
bicycles 6:454; 7:512
Big Bang 1:47; 3:169; 4:261; 5:342, 354, 355; 9:709; 10:727, 770, 771
bimetallic strips 10:739
binary code 3:231
binary stars 1:66–67; 3:209; 7:536; 9:716–717; 10:794
binoculars 6:407
    night vision 5:340
biochemistry 1:68–73; 2:123, 125
biodegradation 10:757
biogenic rocks 9:687
biology, space 9:710–711
biomes 1:74
bioremediation 1:70
biosphere 1:74–75
Bjerknes, Vilhelm and Jacob 7:485
Black Forest 4:280
Black Hills, South Dakota 2:110
black holes 1:67, 76–77; 4:261, 291; 5:327, 347; 7:537; 9:666, 718; 10:771
    and gravity 1:76; 5:327; 9:667
    and quasars 9:651
    and time travel 10:753
Black, Joseph 5:341
Black Sea 5:372, 373
black smokers 5:359

Blanc, Mont 4:257
blast furnace 2:118; 5:378, 379; 6:458, 473; 9:692–693
blood flow, measurement 3:193
blue-shift 1:67; 3:193
body, human, chemicals in 2:120
bogs 10:793
Bohr, Niels 3:228; 8:584; 9:649; 10:726
boiling See evaporation and boiling
Boltwood, Bertram 4:305
Boltzmann, Ludwig 5:341
bombs
    hydrogen/thermonuclear 4:289
    nuclear 1:59; 4:270, 271, 289
bonds, chemical 7:501–502
    covalent 2:150, 151; 5:375; 7:500–501, 502, 503
    hydrogen 2:92; 6:414; 7:503
    ionic 2:150, 151
    in liquids 6:414–415
    London forces 6:415
    metallic 6:468; 7:501
    peptide 1:68
    polar 6:414
    saturated and unsaturated 6:412
bones 1:78
Borchgrevink, Carsten 1:34
boreholes 5:357
bornite 9:693
boron 6:471
boron trichloride 7:503
Bose, S.N. 8:586
Bosporus Strait 5:373
Boutan, Louis 6:442
Boyle, Robert 2:122, 123; 4:293; 8:608–609
Boyle's law 4:293
Brahe, Sofie 1:45, 46; 7:528
Brahe, Tycho 1:45, 46; 5:326; 7:527–528
brass 1:29; 3:165; 6:473
Brattain, Walter 3:231
Braun, Karl Ferdinand 2:107
Braun, Wernher von 1:36; 4:260
Brazil 9:707
Brazil Current 1:50
breakdancing 7:505

breakwaters 2:143
breccias 9:687
bridges, designed 3:211
brighteners 6:419
British Isles 5:380
Broglie, Louis-Victor-Pierre Raymond de 3:227; 9:649
bromine 5:335–336, 337
1-bromo-1-nitroethane 5:382
1-bromo-2-nitroethane 5:382
Brongniart, Alexandre 4:305
Bronsted–Lowry theory 1:11
Bronsted, Johannes 1:11
bronze 1:28, 29; 3:164, 165; 6:472
    aluminum bronze 1:29; 3:165
    manganese bronze 6:437
Bronze Age 6:472
brown dwarfs 10:771
Brownian motion 6:415
Brown, Robert 6:415
Bryce Canyon, Utah 2:112
bubble chambers 3:227; 8:585, 586
Buchner, Eduard 2:123
Buckland, William 4:307
buckminsterfullerene 2:98
bunds 1:13
Bunsen, Robert 9:715
Burgess Shale 2:89
Burnell, Jocelyn Bell 9:647
burning (combustion) 8:573
butane 5:353, 382
butanol, reaction with acetic acid 2:119–120
butene 5:353
butyl acetate 2:119–120

Cabochons 4:301
Caesar, Julius 2:86; 10:749
cairngorm 9:650
Calama 9:663
calcite 6:410; 7:491; 9:673
calcium 1:78; 6:469; 8:594
calcium bicarbonate 2:101; 5:331
calcium carbonate 1:78
    in limestone 6:410, 411
calcium fluoride (fluorite; fluorspar) 1:78; 6:411, 419
calcium hydrogen carbonate 9:677

calcium hydroxide (slaked lime) 1:78; 6:469
calcium hydroxyphosphate 1:78
calcium magnesium carbonate 6:469
calcium oxide (lime; quicklime) 1:78; 6:411, 469
calcium sulfate, hydrated 1:78; 6:469
calculators 3:229, 230
    LCD displays 6:417
calculus 7:528
calderas 3:170, 171
calendars 2:84–87; 4:250; 10:749
California 7:535
    earthquakes 7:534
    Gold Rush (1849) 4:317; 7:494; 8:565
Callisto (moon) 5:388, 389; 9:680, 698
calomel 6:459
caloric 5:341
calories (heat energy) 5:339
Cambrian period 2:88–89; 4:305, 306; 8:580
    North America during 2:89; 8:581
cameras 7:554; 8:604
    camera obscura 8:603
    infrared 5:371
    Schmidt 10:733
Cameroon Highlands 1:19
Canada
    ice ages 5:365
    permafrost 8:596
Canadian Shield 7:533, 535
cancer, skin 8:575; 10:767
Cannizzaro, Stanislao 8:591
canyons 2:90–91; 5:394; 10:774
    submarine 2:90, 91, 158; 6:444
capacitors 3:230
capillary action 2:92–93
capillary effect 2:93
carbohydrates 2:94–96
carbolic acid 8:601
carbon 2:97–99; 7:532
    cycle 1:54
    isotopes 2:97, 108; 5:384, 385; 9:654, 655, 656–657
    and organic compounds 8:566–567
    structure and bonding 2:98
carbon dating See radiocarbon dating
carbon dioxide 2:97, 99, 100–101

Volume numbers appear in **boldface type** followed by colons. Page numbers in **boldface type** refer to main articles and their illustrations. Page numbers in *italic type* refer to additional illustrations.

atmospheric **1:**52, *54*; **2:**100
and deforestation **4:**279, 313
density **3:**183
and global warming **1:**54;
  2:101, 140; **4:**279, *313*–314
solid (dry ice) **2:**100; **3:**195;
  8:606; **9:***701*
and stalactites/stalagmites
  2:101
to make sodas **8:**607
carbon disulfide **2:**99
carbonic acid **2:**99, 100
Carboniferous period **2:**138;
  5:364; **7:**496; **8:**580, 588
  See also Mississippian period;
    Pennsylvanian period
carbon monoxide **2:**97, 99,
  139; **8:**573
carbonyl groups, in sugars **2:**95
carboxylic acid group **1:**68;
  5:355
Caribbean Sea **2:102–103**
Carlsbad Caverns **2:**110; **5:***331*
Carnot, Sadi **8:**611
carotene **5:**352
Carothers, Wallace H. **8:**619,
  620; **10:**731
Carpenter, M. Scott **6:***462*,
  463, 465
Carson, Rachel **5:**336
cartographers **6:**438, 439
carving rigs **7:**493
Cascade Range **7:**515, 535;
  8:577
Caspian Sea **5:**372
catalysts **2:104–105**, 120; **6:**470
catalytic converters **2:***105*;
  4:*313*
cataracts (eye) **8:**575; **10:**767
cathode rays **2:106–107**
cathode-ray tubes **2:**106, *107*;
  3:225, 231
cations **5:**374; **9:**646
CAT scans **10:**798
Cavendish, Henry **2:**123
caves **2:108–111**
  limestone **2:**108, *109*–110;
    5:331; **6:**411
  sea **2:**111; **4:**254
Cayley, George **1:**18
CD players **5:**398; **7:**556
Celanese **10:**731
celestial equator **4:**250, 251
celestial poles **2:**154
celestial sphere **4:**250
cell membranes, and osmosis
  8:568
celluloid **8:**619

cellulose **2:**94; **10:**731
cellulose acetate **10:**731
cellulose lacquer paints **8:**579
cell walls, phospholipids **6:**413
Celsius, Anders **5:**341; **10:**739
Celsius temperature scale
  5:339, 341; **10:**739
cement **6:**469
Cenozoic era **2:112–113**; **4:**305
  periods *See* Quaternary
    period; Tertiary period
centigrade *See* Celsius
  temperature scale
Central America, climate **7:**535
centrifuges **2:***114*, 115; **7:**499
  ultracentrifuges **1:**69
centripetal and centrifugal
  forces **2:**114–115
  at the equator **3:**199
  ultracentrifuges **1:**69
cephalopods **5:**391
Cepheid variables **1:**47
cerargyrite **9:**690
ceratopsians **3:**173
Ceres (asteroid) **1:**42; **9:**696
Cernan, Eugene **4:**298
cesium **6:**468; **9:**715
cetyl palmitate **6:**413
CFCs *See* chlorofluorocarbons
Chad, Lake **1:**22
Chadwick, James **7:**526; **8:**584;
  10:726
Chaffee, Roger **1:**37
Chagos Laccadive Plateau
  5:369
chain reactions **4:**270; **6:**407
  and fusion **4:**288
chalcopyrite **6:**472; **9:**693
chalk **1:**78; **3:**172, 173; **6:**410;
  9:687
Challenger (space shuttle)
  7:*518*, 519
Challenger Deep **6:**444
Challenger, HMS **6:**443; **7:**547
Chancourtois, Alexandre-
  Emile Beguyer de **8:**591
Channeled Scablands **2:**113;
  5:363
charcoal **2:**97
charge-couple devices (CCDs)
  10:735
Charles, Jacques-Alexandre-
  César **4:**293; **8:**609
Charles's law **4:**293
Charon **8:**624–625; **9:**699
charts, nautical **6:**439
chemical reactions **2:**104,
  116–120; **6:**451

activation energy **2:**104, 105
displacement reactions **8:**571
equations **2:**117, 124–125
luminescent **6:**419
oxidation **8:570–571**, 572
produced by light **6:**407
reversible **2:**118
speed **2:**117
See also catalysts
chemistry **2:121–125**
organic **2:**125, 139; **8:566–567**
physical **2:**125; **8:608–609**
Chernobyl **4:**271; **9:***654*
Cherrapunji **7:***507*; **9:**663
Chesapeake Bay **2:**141
Chichén Itzá **4:**251
Chicxulub, meteorite impact
  4:*265*
Chile, earthquake **3:**207
China
  calendar **2:**87
  floods **4:**273
  mapmaking **6:**439
Chinooks **10:**797
Chiquicamata, Chile **3:**165
chirality **5:**383
Chiron **9:**696
Chladni, Ernst **6:**478
chlorides **9:**677
chlorine **2:**150; **5:**335, 337
  bonding **7:**502
  as a free radical **5:**375
  poisons **5:**336
  reaction with sodium
    2:118–119; **5:**374–375;
    8:571
  relative atomic mass **5:**384
chlorofluorocarbons
(CFCs) **1:**33; **5:**337

environmental effects **1:**53,
  75; **4:**314; **5:**337; **8:***574*,
  575, 601, 631
chlorophyll **2:**94, 101; **6:**429;
  8:571
cholesteric liquid crystals
  6:417
cholesteryl benzoate **6:**416
chondrites **6:**478
chromatography **2:**93
chromium, in steel alloys **5:**379
chronometers **3:**179; **10:**751
cinder cones **10:***781*
cinnabar **6:**459
circuits
  electric **1:**64; **3:**213
  electronic **3:**229–*230*
  integrated *See* integrated
    circuits
cirques/corries **2:**129; **4:**254,
  311–312; **5:**392, 395
cis- isomers **5:**383
citric acid **1:**10, *71*
Clairaut, Alexis **2:**149
Clavius, Christoph **2:**86;
  10:*749*
clay **2:126–127**
cleavage **4:**301; **7:**491
Clementine (space probe) **6:**423;
  7:510; **9:**669
cliffs **2:128–129**, 142
  caves **2:**111
climate **2:130–133**
  and erosion **4:**252

An object thrown (launched) at a certain velocity goes into orbit around Earth.

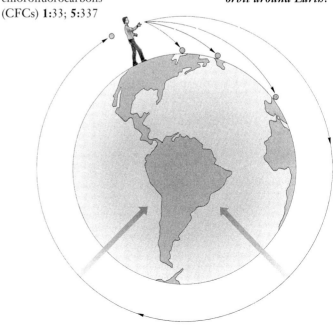

fluctuations **4:**315
  and forests **4:**280
  and grasslands **5:**324–325
  and the Gulf Stream **5:**334
  Paleozoic **8:**581
  past **4:**315; **5:**362–365
  and water **5:**357
  See also deserts; global
    warming; ice ages;
    weather; winds
clocks **10:**749–751
cloud chambers **3:**226
clouds **2:**134–137; **7:**486;
  9:662–663; **10:***724,* 790
  cumulonimbus
    (thunderclouds) **2:***135,*
    137; **6:**408–409
  and meteorology **7:**485
  seeding **3:**195; **9:**691
clusters, galaxy **4:**290, 291
coal **2:**98, **138–140;** **4:**283
  coal-fired power plants **3:**215
  formation **1:**54; **2:***139,* 140;
    8:589; **9:**687
  mining **2:**139–140; **7:***492,* 493
coal gas **2:**139; **8:**601
coal tar **2:**139
coasts **2:141–143;** **5:**395; **7:**541
  beaches **9:**679; **10:**787
  floods **4:**273
cobalt **5:**378, 385; **6:**434–435;
  9:655
cocaine **1:**26, 27
coccoliths **9:**687
cochineal **3:**196
coconut oil **6:***412*
codeine **1:**26
codons **1:**73
coelacanths **2:**111
coesite **6:**475
coke **2:**98, 138–139
collagen **9:**645
Collins, Michael **1:***37,* 38;
  4:298
collodion **8:**604
color **2:144–147;** **3:**218; **6:**404;
  7:553
  photography **2:**147; **3:**197;
    8:*605*
  See also dyes; pigments
color blindness **2:**146
Colorado River **2:**90–91, 129;
  7:533–534; **10:**740
Columbia (space shuttle) **9:***711*
Columbia River **3:***199*
Columbus, Christopher **4:**302
combustion (burning) **8:**573
combustion analysis **8:**567

comets **1:**42; **2:148–149;** **9:**697
  meteoroids from **6:**478
compasses, magnetic **6:**430,
    433; **8:**638
compounds **2:150–151**
Compton effect **9:**649
computers **3:**229, 230
  binary code **3:**231
  and oceanography **7:**549
  optical **4:**269; **7:**556
  screens **6:***416,* 417, 419;
    7:556
  and weather forecasts **7:**486
Concepción **10:**745
Concorde (aircraft) **1:**14, 17
condensation **8:**606; **10:**784
condensation reactions
    1:68–69
condensers **4:**259
conductance, electrical **3:**213
conduction, heat **4:**247; **5:**340
conductors, electrical **1:**31;
    3:213, 215; **9:**701
  and temperature **10:**738–739
conglomerates **9:**687
Congo River **1:**21
Conrad, Charles "Pete" **1:**38;
    4:297, 299
constellations **2:152–155;**
    4:250; **9:**716, 717, 718
contact forces **4:**276, *277*
continental climate **2:**132
continental drift **2:**156–157;
    3:202; **8:**582, 622–623
continental margins **7:**540
continental rise **7:**540
continental shelves **1:**49;
    2:158; **7:**540
continental slopes **7:**540
continents **2:156–157**
  edges *See* continental shelves
  supercontinents *See*
    Gondwana; Laurasia;
    Pangaea
contour lines **6:**440
contrails **2:**137
convection (heat) **4:**247; **5:**340
  and the weather **7:**485
  See also convection currents
convection currents
  air **5:***339,* 340
  in the Earth's mantle **3:**202,
    203, 204

converters, catalytic **2:***105;*
    4:*313*
Cook, James **1:**34; **6:**442
Cooper, L. Gordon **4:**297;
    6:463, 465
Copernicus, Nicolaus **1:**45;
    3:*169,* 198
copper **3:164–165;** **6:***468;* **7:**491
  blister **9:**693
  compounds **3:**164–165; **8:***594*
  electrical conductance **3:***164,*
    165, 215
  extraction **2:**121; **6:**472;
    9:693
  purification **3:**217
copper chloride **3:**165
copper (I) oxide (cuprous
    oxide) **3:**164; **7:***501*
copper (II) oxide (cupric oxide)
    3:165
copper (II) sulfate (cupric
    sulfate) **3:**165
coral reefs **2:**103, 143; **5:***395;*
    8:581
  Devonian period **3:**189
  threats to **2:***103*
corals **7:**558
core, Earth's **3:**199, *201,* 202–203
Coriolis effect **1:**25; **5:**350;
    10:790, 795
Coriolis, Gaspard-Gustave de
    1:25; **10:**795
Corliss, Jack **5:**359
corries *See* cirques/corries
Cort, Henry **5:**379
Cosmic Background Explorer
    (COBE) **4:**261
cosmic dust collectors **6:**446
cosmic rays **1:**53; **3:166–167,** 226
cosmology **3:168–169**
Cottonwood caves, New
    Mexico **2:**110
Coulomb, Charles-Augustin de
    4:276; **6:**433
Courtelle **10:**731
Courtois, Bernard **5:**335
Cousteau, Jacques-Yves **6:**441;
    7:547
Crab Nebula **9:***647*
Crab Pulsar **9:***647*
cracking processes **8:**601
craters **3:170–171**
  impact **3:**170–171; **6:**476–477

lunar **3:**171, 198; **7:**509, 510
Cretaceous period **3:172–173;**
    4:265 **6:**467, 476
Crete **2:**129; **10:**745
crevasses, glacial **4:**312
Crick, Francis **1:**73
crinoids **7:**496
Crookes, William **2:**107;
    3:225
crops, spraying **3:**233
Cros, Charles **8:**605
crust, Earth's **3:**199–200, *201*
cryogenics **3:174–175**
cryolite **1:**30
cryosurgery **3:**175
crystals **3:176–177;** **4:**301;
    9:700–701
  grown in space **9:**711
  ice **5:**361
  liquid crystals **6:416–417**
  See also gemstones
crystal systems **7:**491
Cuba **2:**102
cupellation **6:**473
cuprammonium ion **3:**165
curare **1:**26
curarine **1:**26
Curie, Pierre and Marie **9:***655*
curine **1:**26
curium **8:**595
currents, ocean *See* ocean
    currents
Cutting, James Ambrose **8:**604
Cuvier, Georges **4:**305, 306
cyclists, aerodynamics **1:***15,* 18
cyclohexane **5:***353*
cyclones **4:**273; **5:**350; **10:***790*
  See also hurricanes
cyclonite (RDX) **4:**263
cyclopropane **2:**99
cyclotrons **3:**235
Cygnid meteors **6:**477
Cygnus X-1 **1:**77
Cyprus **3:**164
cytosine **1:**71–72

Dachstein **2:**110
Dacron **10:**731
Daguerre, Louis **8:**603–604
daguerreotypes **8:**603–604
Dalton, John **1:***55*–56;
    2:124–125; **6:**451; **8:**583, 590
dams **4:**272–273; **5:**393
Daniell, John Frederic **1:**65
Darwin, Charles **4:**283; **6:**442
dating
  radiocarbon *See* radiocarbon
    dating

Volume numbers appear in **boldface type** followed by
colons. Page numbers in **boldface type** refer to main
articles and their illustrations. Page numbers in *italic type*
refer to additional illustrations.

rocks **4:**304–305, 307; **6:**431; **8:**634; **9:**656
Davis, William Morris **5:**394
Davy, Humphry **1:**65, 78; **5:**335, 341; **6:**428
days **3:**178–179, 203
solar **2:**84; **3:**178
DDT **5:**336
dead rooms **1:**14
Dead Sea **5:**373
Death Valley, California **4:**255; **7:**533
Deccan plateau **10:**741
deceleration **4:**277
decibels **1:**14
decompression sickness **6:**442
Deep Flight (submersible) **7:**549
Deep Rover (submersible) **7:**549
Deepstar 4000 (submersible) **6:**444
deforestation **4:**279, 313; **5:**357; **10:**761
de Forest, Lee **3:**231
Deimos (moon) **1:**43; **6:**449; **9:**680
deltas **2:**143; **3:**180–181; **4:**253; **9:**671; **10:**793
De Materia Medica **1:**27
Democritus **1:**55; **2:**122; **6:**451; **8:**583, 613
dendrochronology **9:**657
Deneb **2:**154, 155
density **1:**25; **3:**182–183
deoxyribonucleic acid *See* DNA
deposition **2:**142–143; **4:**253
De Re Metallica (book) **7:**492
desalination **8:**569
Descartes, René **3:**169; **7:**557
deserts **1:**74; **2:**132; **3:**184–185, 194, *195*; **5:***333*
erosion **3:**185; **4:**254–255
mirages in **7:***495*
sand dunes **3:**185; **9:**679
desert varnish **3:**185
detergents **3:**186–187; **10:**730
See also soaps
detrital rocks **9:**687
deuterium **5:**354
and fusion **4:**288–289
Deville, Henri Saint-Claire **1:**30
Devonian period **3:**188–189; **8:***580*
Dewar flasks **3:**175
Dewar, James **3:**175
dew point **2:**134; **5:**349
dialysis **10:**757

diamond **2:**97–98, *99*; **3:**177; **4:**300, 301; **7:**491
diborane **6:**471
1,2-dibromoethene **5:**383
diffraction
light **6:**406; **7:**554, *556*
sound **1:**12; **9:**705
diffusion **3:**190–191; **4:**294–295
See also osmosis
dimensions **9:**708; **10:**752, 753
compacted/invisible **4:**276
dimers **8:**633
dimethyl ether **5:**382
2,2-dimethylpropane **5:**382
dinitrobenzene, isomers **5:**383
dinosaurs **3:**173; **5:***390, 391*
extinction **1:**43; **2:**149; **3:**171, 173; **4:**265; **6:**476
fossils **4:**283, 285
Jurassic **6:**467
Mesozoic **6:***466*
diodes **3:**230, 231; **9:**688
light-emitting (LEDs) **3:**230; **4:**247
Dionysius Exiguus **2:**87
Dioscorides **1:**27
dioxins **1:**70; **5:**336; **8:**601
dipoles, molecular **8:**627
Dirac, Paul **3:**226; **8:**584–585
direct current (DC) **3:**213
disaccharides **2:**95–96
discharge tubes **2:**106; **3:**220–221; **4:**295
Discovery (space shuttle) **5:**347
diseases **1:**73; **10:**761
displacement reactions **8:**571
distance, measured using lasers **5:**398
distillation **2:**120, 122; **4:**259; **8:**607
air **8:**573
of coal tar **2:**139
destructive **2:**138–139
fractional **7:**499; **8:**573
for refining **9:**665
diving **6:***441–442*, 444; **7:**547
and helium **5:**342
diving bells **5:**369
diving suits **7:**547
DNA (deoxyribonucleic acid) **1:**71–72; **4:**283; **6:**417; **10:***767*
and protein formation **1:**73; **9:**645
structure **1:***69*, 72–73; **7:**502
docking, in space **4:***297*–298
dolines *See* swallow holes

dolomite **6:**411, 429, 469
dolostone **6:**411
domains **5:**378; **6:**435
Dominica **2:**103
doping **9:**688
Doppler, Christian Johann **3:**192
Doppler effect **3:**192–193
and astronomy **1:**47; **3:**193; **10:**769
downdrafts **10:**795
downwellings **7:**541, *543*
drag **1:**15, 17
drainage basins **5:**395
Drakensberg Mountains **1:**19
Dresser, Heinrich **1:**27
dressing, ores **9:**692
drizzle **9:**663
drought **3:**194–195, 237; **4:**280
drugs (medicinal)
alkaloid **1:**26, 27
isomers **5:**383
medicinal compounds **6:**429
ocean sources **6:**444
drumlins **2:**113; **4:**312
dry ice **2:**100; **3:**195; **8:**606; **9:***701*
dry washes *See* wadis
Ducos du Hauron, Louis **8:**605
Du Fay, Charles **3:**233
dunes **2:**143; **3:**185; **9:**679
Du Pont, E.I. **4:**263
dust, interplanetary **6:**477
dust bowl **3:**195
dustdevils **10:**754
dust storms **4:**255
dyes **3:**196–197; **8:**621
See also paints; pigments
dykes **5:**367; **6:**427, 474–475
dynamite **7:**493
dynamo, Earth as a **6:**431

Earle, Sylvia A. **7:***549*
Earth **3:**198–203; **9:**695
age **4:**305, 307
circumference **4:**302
distance from the Sun **9:**697
flat or round? **3:**200
gravity **1:**23; **3:**199; **4:**275; **5:**328

infrared images of **5:***370*
magnetism **6:***430*–431, 435; **9:**657
orbit **2:**86; **3:**203
seasons **9:**684–685
structure **3:**199–200, *201*, 202–203
surface without oceans **4:***303*
tilt **2:**130; **3:**203; **4:**250
time zones **3:***178*, 179; **10:***751*
See also atmosphere
earthflows **4:**255
earthquakes **3:**204–207; **4:**257, 266, *267*
in North America **3:**204–205, *207*; **4:**267; **7:**534
and tidal waves **3:**205; **10:**744
Earthshine **7:**509
easterlies **10:**788, 797
Eastman, George **8:**604–605
East Pacific Rise **5:**359
echoes **1:**12, 13; **9:**704
echolocation **10:**764
eclipses **3:**208–209
lunar **3:**200, 209; **7:***509*
solar **3:***208–209*; **7:**509
ecliptic **2:**153, 155; **4:**250
Edison, Thomas Alva **3:**214; **6:**406; **8:**605; **9:**705
Edward, Lake **1:**22
Egyptians, ancient **1:**44; **2:**85, 121; **3:**168
Eiffel, Gustave **3:**165
Einstein, Albert
and Brownian motion **6:**415
and electromagnetism **6:**434
and energy **4:**248, 271; **6:**450
general theory of relativity

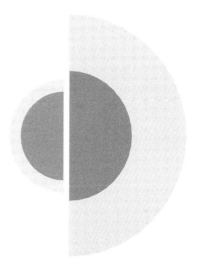

Comparison of Mercury's core (left) to that of Earth (right).

(theory of gravity)
4:275–276; 5:327, 328;
8:612; 9:667
and light 3:227; 9:649
mass-energy equation 4:271
and the nuclear bomb 4:271
and the photoelectric effect
8:602
and space 10:771
special theory of relativity
8:611–612; 9:666–667,
709
einsteinium 8:595
Eisenhower, Dwight D.
6:462–463; 7:516
Eisreisenwelt 2:110
elasticity 3:210–211
El Chinchonal 2:133
electricity 3:212–215, 229
conductors and insulators
3:213; 9:701
electrostatics 3:212–213,
232–233
from fuel cells 5:355
from geysers 4:309
in lightning 6:408–409
and magnetism See
electromagnetism
solar 3:215
superconductors 3:175;
10:739
See also batteries; power
plants
electrocardiographs 2:107
electrodes 1:64
electrolysis 1:78; 3:216–217;
4:317; 9:665
for metal extraction 6:473
to produce magnesium 6:428
electrolytes 3:216
electromagnetic induction
3:223
electromagnetic spectrum
3:218–221; 5:370
and remote sensing 9:668–669
See also gamma rays; infrared
radiation; light;
microwaves; radio waves;
ultraviolet radiation;
X rays
electromagnetism 3:222–224;
4:276; 6:433–434; 8:611
particles carrying 8:585
See also magnetic poles
electromagnets 2:107; 3:222,
223–224; 6:436
electromotive force (EMF)
3:223

electronegativity 8:627
electronics 3:229–231
electron microprobes 7:491
electrons 3:225–228
in atoms 1:56; 2:107, 145;
3:227–228, 234–235;
5:396–397; 6:418, 434;
8:583, 584
behaving as waves 3:227, 228
charge 3:227
cosmic ray 3:167
discovery 1:56; 2:107; 3:225;
8:584; 10:725
and electricity 3:213, 215
and lasers 5:396–397
and luminescence 6:418
mass 1:56
orbits/shells/energy levels
5:396–397; 8:584; 9:714
positive See positrons
in semiconductors 9:688
See also electronics
electroplating 3:216, 217;
9:691
electrostatics 3:212–213, 232–233
elements 2:124, 150;
3:234–235; 8:583
of the Greek philosophers
2:122; 4:275
half-life 4:307; 9:656
native 7:491
oxidation numbers
8:570–571
table of See periodic table
See also isotopes
elevators, and weight 10:791
El Niño and La Niña
3:236–238; 7:547; 8:576, 577
emeralds 4:300, 301
Empedocles 2:122, 124
emulsions 7:498–499
enantiomers 5:383
Endeavour (space shuttle) 5:347
endorphins 1:27
energy 4:244–248
activation 2:104, 105
from the oceans 6:444
internal 4:246–247
kinetic 3:215; 4:246, 247,
248; 5:339
law of conservation of 4:245,
246, 248; 8:611; 10:743
new souces of 7:551

potential 3:215; 4:245, 247,
248
See also fission, nuclear;
fusion, nuclear
engines 5:345
jet 6:453
Eniwetok Atoll 4:289
ENSO 3:236–237
entropy 10:743, 753
enzymes 1:71; 2:104, 105, 120;
9:645
are proteins 2:123
in detergent products 3:187
proteolytic 3:187
Eocene epoch 2:112; 10:740,
741
eons, geologic 4:304; 8:634
epicycles, theory of 1:45
epochs, geologic 4:304
Epsom salts 6:429
equator 3:199
celestial 4:250, 251
equatorial currents 1:49
equinoxes and solstices 2:86;
3:179; 4:249–251; 9:685
equivalence, principle of 5:328
eras 2:87
geologic 4:304; 6:466
Eratosthenes 4:302; 6:439
ergonovine 1:26
ergospheres 1:77
Erie, Lake 5:392
erosion 4:252–523; 9:687
cliff 2:128–129
coastal 2:142; 7:541
and deforestation 4:279
in deserts 3:185; 4:254–255
by flowing water 4:252–253;
9:671; 10:785
forming clay 2:127
by glaciers 4:253–254, 311,
312; 5:395
and landforms 5:395
mass wasting 4:255
soil 3:195; 4:255
by waves 2:142; 4:254
by wind 3:185; 4:255
"Eskimo" nebula 9:717
esters 6:412
estuaries 3:181; 9:670
and pollution 2:142
ethane 2:99; 5:352, 353
ethanol 5:382

ethene 5:352, 353
ether (hypothetical medium)
9:709
ethers 8:567
Ethiopia, lakes 5:393
Ethiopian Highlands 1:19
ethylbutene 5:353
ethylenediamine tetra-acetate
(EDTA) 2:151
ethyne 5:352
Euclid of Alexandria 7:556
Euphrates River 4:272
Eurasia 4:256–257
Europa (moon) 5:388, 389;
9:680, 698; 10:783
eurypterids 7:558
evaporation and boiling
4:258–259
boiling 4:258, 259; 6:415,
457
evaporation 4:258–259; 5:348,
356; 8:606
evaporites 8:598–599; 9:687
event horizon 1:77
Everest, Mount 3:200; 4:257;
7:514
evolution 4:282–283, 283; 5:381
exosphere 1:54; 5:386
expansion, thermal 9:700
Explorer probes 4:260–261
explosives 4:262–263
for mining 7:492–493
to discover oil fields 7:551
extinction 4:264–265, 305; 6:467
and extraterrestrial impacts
1:43; 2:149; 3:171, 173;
4:264; 6:467, 476
Jurassic 5:390
Quaternary 9:653
Triassic 10:758, 759
Extreme Ultraviolet Explorer
(EUVE) 4:261
Exxon Valdez oil spill 1:70;
8:631
eyes, vision 2:145–146;
7:552–553, 555

Fabrics, brighteners 6:419
Faith 7 (spacecraft) 6:465
famine 3:194
Faraday, Michael
and electromagnetism 3:214,
219, 222, 223, 224; 6:434;
8:611
isolation of magnesium
6:428
Farenheit, Daniel 5:341;
10:739

Volume numbers appear in **boldface type** followed by colons. Page numbers in **boldface type** refer to main articles and their illustrations. Page numbers in *italic type* refer to additional illustrations.

Farenheit temperature scale **5**:339, 341; **10**:739
Fata Morgana **7**:495
fatigue **3**:211
fats and oils **6**:412, 413
  fats measured in food mixtures **7**:499
  saturated and unsaturated **6**:*412*–413
fatty acids **6**:412
faults **4**:266–267; **7**:*515*
  and metamorphic rocks **6**:475
fault traps **7**:*522*
feldspars **5**:366; **9**:673
fens **10**:793
fermentation **2**:105, 123
Fermi, Enrico **4**:271; **7**:526, 539; **8**:626
ferric oxide (rust) **5**:379; **8**:*570*
ferromagnetism **5**:378; **6**:434–435
ferromanganese **6**:437
fertilizers **1**:75; **2**:103; **7**:531; **8**:631
fetch **10**:786
fiberglass **8**:621
fiber optics **4**:268–269; **5**:398; **7**:556
fibers, synthetic **10**:**731**
fiberscopes **4**:*269*
Fiji islands **7**:544
fillings, tooth **1**:*29*
filtration **7**:499
Fingal's Cave **2**:111
fireflies **6**:419
fires, grassland **5**:325
fireworks **4**:262
Fischer, Emil **1**:69; **2**:95
fish **3**:188, 189; **7**:496; **8**:*580*
fishing **1**:*49*; **6**:444
fission, nuclear **4**:248, **270–271**, 289
  See also fusion, nuclear
fjords **2**:129, 142; **4**:254; **9**:*652*
flashlights **1**:64
Fleming, John Ambrose **3**:231
flight, aircraft **1**:*16*–17, *18*
flood basalt eruptions **10**:781
floods **3**:195; **4**:272–273; **9**:671
  biblical **5**:364
  flash **3**:184; **4**:272
Florida Current **5**:334
flotation **6**:473; **8**:565; **9**:692
  of toxic waste **10**:756–757
flowstone deposits **2**:110
fluid dynamics **1**:17–18
fluorescence **3**:197, 219; **6**:418, 419

fluorine **5**:335, 336, 337
fluorite *See* calcium fluoride
fluorspar *See* calcium fluoride
flywheels **7**:505
focal length **10**:733–734
fog **5**:349; **7**:*499*
fold mountains **7**:*515*
food, freezing **5**:*361*
foods
  carbohydrates in **2**:*95*
  genetically modified (GM) **1**:73
footprints, fossilized **4**:283–284
Forbes, Edward **6**:442
force multipliers **6**:454
forces **4**:274–277
  and particles **8**:585
  See also electromagnetism; gravity; strong nuclear force; weak nuclear force
forensic science **6**:419; **9**:705; **10**:767
forests **4**:278–281; **10**:737, 761
  deforestation **4**:*279*, 313; **5**:357; **10**:761
formic acid **1**:10
formulas, chemical **2**:117
fossil fuels *See* fuels, fossil
fossils **4**:282–285; **9**:686
  Cambrian **2**:*88*–89
  in caves **2**:108
  and continental drift **8**:622–623
  Cretceous **3**:173
  Devonian period **8**:*580*
  and geologic timescale **4**:305, 306
  human **1**:22; **4**:283–284
  index **4**:305
  Jurassic **4**:*284*; **6**:467
  and limestone **6**:410, *411*
  magnetism **6**:431
  Mississippian **7**:496
  Ordovician **7**:*558*
  Paleozoic **8**:*580*
  Precambrian **8**:*635*
  Silurian **9**:*689*
  and supercontinents **2**:157; **4**:318
Foucault, Jean **6**:407
francium **6**:468
Franklin, Benjamin **3**:233; **5**:334; **6**:442; **8**:611
Franklin, Rosalind **1**:*72*–73
Fraunhofer, Joseph von **1**:47; **9**:*715*
Freedom 7 (spacecraft) **6**:464, 465

free falling **10**:*791*
free radicals **5**:375; **6**:412
freezing, cryogenic **3**:175
frequency **3**:218, 221; **9**:703; **10**:764
frescoes **8**:578
Fresnel, Augustin **6**:405
friction **4**:274, **286–287**
Friendship 7 (spacecraft) **6**:465
fronts, weather **2**:135; **6**:439; **7**:485; **9**:663; **10**:789
frost **5**:*360*, 361
fructose **2**:95, *96*
fuel, hydrogen as a **5**:355
fuel cells **5**:355
fuels, fossil **1**:54; **4**:283; **7**:550–551
  burning **1**:75; **8**:573
  in continental shelves **2**:158
  See also coal; natural gas; oil, crude
Fuji, Mount **7**:514; **10**:780
Fujita–Pearson scale **10**:755, 796
fulcrums **6**:*454*
Fuller, Buckminster **2**:98
fullerene **2**:98
functional groups **8**:567
Fundy, Bay of **10**:747
fusion, latent heat of **5**:341
fusion, nuclear **3**:235; **4**:248, **288–289**; **8**:617
  in the Sun/stars **4**:*288*; **5**:327; **6**:450; **7**:536; **9**:664, 694

Gabbro **6**:427; **9**:672
Gagarin, Yuri **9**:674, *675*

Gahn, Johan **6**:437
Galápagos Rift **5**:359
galaxies **3**:169, 193; **4**:290–291; **10**:770
  and quasars **9**:651
  See also Milky Way
galena **7**:491; **8**:564; **9**:693
Galilee, Sea of **5**:393
Galilei, Galileo **8**:610
  astronomical observations **1**:45; **3**:169, 198; **7**:509, 525; **9**:708
  and gravity **4**:275; **5**:326; **7**:513, 527
  ideas about force and motion **4**:274; **7**:513
  and the pendulum **10**:749–750
  telescope **10**:733, *734*
Galileo (space probe) **1**:43; **5**:389; **7**:*508*, *517*, 519
Galle, John Gottfried **7**:525
gallium **8**:594
Galvani, Luigi **3**:213–214
galvanized iron **5**:379
galvanometers **6**:434
Galveston Island **7**:521
gamma rays **3**:221; **5**:385; **8**:638; **9**:655; **10**:729
  and positrons **3**:226
  and remote sensing **9**:669
Ganges River **3**:180
  delta **3**:181; **4**:273
gangue **8**:564, 565; **9**:692

The Sun's light is partly reflected and partly refracted (bent) by water.

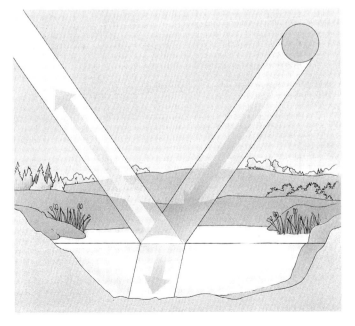

Ganymede (moon) **5**:388, 389;
 9:680, 698
gases **4**:292–295; **6**:*451*; **9**:700
 atmospheric **1**:52, 59; **2**:100
 density **3**:183
 diffusion **3**:190, 191; **4**:294–295
 gas laws **4**:292, 293, 294;
  8:608–609, 637
 mixtures **7**:498, *499*
 motion around objects
  See aerodynamics
 noble/inert **4**:*295*; **5**:342;
  7:500, 502, 532
gasoline **2**:105; **3**:183; **8**:600–601
Gaspra (asteroid) **1**:43
gauge bosons **8**:585, 586
Gay-Lussac, Joseph **5**:335
gears **6**:454, 455
Geiger counters **3**:166, 167;
 8:638
Geiger, Hans **3**:166
Gell-Mann, Murray **8**:586,
 613; **10**:727
Gemini missions **4**:296–299;
 7:518
gemstones **4**:300–301; **9**:650,
 700–701
 See also crystals
General Circulation Models
 (GCMs) **4**:314
generators **3**:224; **6**:434
genes **1**:73; **9**:645
genetic engineering **1**:70, 73
genetics **1**:71–72
gentian violet **3**:197
geochemistry **4**:307
geodynamo **6**:431
Geographia **4**:302
Geographica **4**:302
geography **4**:302–303
geoids **4**:261
geological surveys **5**:371
geologic timescale **4**:304–305,
 306–307
geology **4**:306–307
geomorphology **5**:394
geophysics **4**:307; **8**:612
GEOS satellites **4**:261
germanium **6**:471; **8**:594
geysers **4**:308–309; **5**:331
Geysir **4**:309
Giacobini–Zinner, Comet
 4:261
Gibbs, John Willard **8**:609
Gibraltar, Straits of **6**:456
Gilbert, William **3**:233; **6**:430,
 433
glaciers **4**:310–312; **5**:361; **9**:653

and cliffs **2**:129
 erosion by **4**:253–254, 311,
  312; **5**:395
 and fjords **2**:129, 142; **9**:*652*
 glacier caves **2**:110
 ice age **5**:362, 363, 364, 367
 and ice avalanches **1**:63
 and lake formation **5**:392
 and supercontinents **4**:318
 in valleys **2**:129, 142; **4**:*306*,
  307, 311
glass **7**:501
glauconite **9**:679
Glenn, John H. **6**:463, *465*
Global Ocean Ecosystem
 Dynamics Program **7**:548
global warming **2**:101, 133,
  140; **3**:195, 238; **4**:313–315
 and deserts **3**:185
 during the Cretaceous **4**:265
 and glaciers **4**:312
 reducing **4**:315
 and sea level **2**:157; **4**:312,
  315
GLORIA (sonar device) **9**:*705*
Glossopteris (seed fern) **8**:*598*,
 599, 622
glowworms **6**:419
glucose **2**:*94*, 95, *96*, 151
gluons **8**:585, 586; **10**:727
glycerol **6**:412
glycogen **2**:96
gneiss **5**:381; **6**:475; **8**:635;
 9:650
Gobi Desert **3**:184
gold **2**:122; **4**:316–317; **6**:470
 gold rushes **1**:61; **4**:*317*;
  7:494; **8**:565
 mining or panning for **4**:317;
  6:473; **7**:493, *494*; **8**:565
 "yellow" **9**:691
Goldstein, Eugen **2**:106–107
Gold, Thomas **9**:647
Gondwana **2**:89, 157; **4**:318;
 5:369, 390; **7**:558; **8**:582,
 588, 589
 and Africa **1**:19
 and Antarctica **1**:33
 and Australia **1**:61
Goode's projection **4**:303
gorges **4**:252; **6**:411; **10**:775
Graham, Thomas **4**:295
Grand Bahama Banks **6**:411

Grand Banks **1**:49; **2**:158
Grand Canyon **2**:*90*–91, 129;
 7:533–534; **10**:*768*, 774
grand unification theories
 (GUTs) **4**:276
granite **3**:199–200; **5**:366
 6:426, 427, 475; **7**:490
 boulders **9**:*672*
Grant, Ulysses S. **7**:521
graphite **2**:97, *98*; **7**:*532*; **9**:701
graptolites **7**:558; **9**:689
grasses, Cenozoic **2**:112
grasslands **5**:324–5; **10**:737
gravitation, universal constant
 of **4**:275
gravitational slingshot **10**:782
gravitometers **8**:638
gravitons **8**:585
gravity **4**:274–276; **5**:326–328;
 7:527; **8**:612
 acceleration due to
  5:327–328
 artificial **5**:328
 and black holes **1**:76; **5**:327;
  9:667
 carrier particles for **8**:585
 Earth's **3**:199; **4**:275; **5**:*328*
 law of universal gravitation
  4:275; **5**:326–327; **7**:513,
  528–529
 and motion **5**:327; **7**:513
 in space **9**:710, *711*; **10**:791
 See also relativity, general
  theory of
grease **3**:*186*
 and soap **6**:413
Great Artesian Basin **5**:331–332
Great Barrier Reef **5**:395
Great Dividing Range **1**:60
Greater Antilles **2**:102
Great Lakes **2**:113, 131; **5**:*392*;
 9:653
 Fata Morgana mirage **7**:495
Great Nevada Basin **7**:535
Great Plains **3**:195; **4**:255;
 5:*332*; **7**:535
Great Rift Valley **1**:19, 21;
 4:266, 285; **8**:623
 lakes **1**:21–22
Great Salt Lake **5**:393
Greeks, ancient **2**:121–122; **3**:233
 astronomy **1**:44–45
 and geography **4**:302

mapmaking **6**:439
 and matter **6**:451
 and the Universe **3**:*168*–169
greenhouse effect **1**:54; **2**:133,
 140; **4**:313–314
Greenland **3**:185, 189; **4**:310,
 311; **5**:381; **8**:635
Greenwich Mean Time
 (GMT) **3**:179; **10**:751
Greenwich Meridian **6**:439
Gregory XIII, Pope **2**:86, *87*;
 10:749
Griess, Johann Peter **3**:197
Grissom, Virgil "Gus" **1**:37;
 4:297; **6**:463, *464*, 465
groins **2**:143
groundwater **5**:329–333, 357
Grove, William **1**:65
guanine **1**:71–72
gulches **10**:775
Gulf Stream **1**:50; **2**:131;
 5:334; **6**:442; **7**:542
gunpowder **4**:*262*, 263;
 7:492–493
Gutenberg, Beno **3**:201, 203
Gutenberg discontinuity
 3:201, 203
GUTs (grand unification
 theories) **4**:276
gypsum **1**:78; **6**:469;
 8:598–599; **9**:687
gyres **1**:49; **7**:543; **8**:576–577
gyroscopes **5**:347; **7**:505

Haber, Fritz **7**:531
Haber process **2**:105; **5**:355;
 7:531
Hadley, George **1**:25
hadrons **8**:586
hadrosaurs **3**:173
Hagomoro (space probe) **6**:423
Hahn, Otto **4**:270–271
Haicheng, earthquake **3**:207
hail **5**:361; **10**:790
Haise, Fred **1**:39
Hale–Bopp comet **2**:*149*
half-life **4**:307; **9**:656
halides **7**:491
halite **8**:598–599
Hall, Charles Martin **1**:30
Halley, Edmond **2**:149;
 7:528
Halley's Comet **2**:149; **8**:616
halogens **5**:335–337
hardness, scale of **4**:301; **7**:491
Harrison, John **6**:442; **10**:751
Hawaiian Islands **3**:201; **7**:515,
 545; **8**:*577*

Volume numbers appear in **boldface type** followed by colons. Page numbers in **boldface type** refer to main articles and their illustrations. Page numbers in *italic type* refer to additional illustrations.

caves **2**:110
volcanoes **2**:110; **3**:170;
10:781
Hawkes, Graham **7**:549
headlands, coastal **2**:142; **4**:254
headphones **1**:14
headwinds **5**:386
heart disease, treatment **4**:263
heat **4**:248; **5**:338–341; **10**:738
and friction **4**:286
heat capacity **5**:340
history of the study of **5**:340,
341
and internal energy
4:246–247
kinetic theory of **5**:341
latent **5**:340–341; **8**:606
radiation *See* infrared
radiation
solar **5**:341
transference **4**:247;
5:338–339, 340
See also temperature(s);
thermodynamics
Heaviside, Oliver **5**:377
Heisenberg, Werner Karl
9:649
helicopters, flight **1**:*18*
heliopause **9**:695
helium **1**:57; **3**:183; **4**:295;
5:342; **8**:*583*
and fusion **4**:*288*–289; **6**:450
in the Universe **7**:532
Hell's Canyon **2**:91
hematite **5**:379; **6**:431; **7**:491;
8:*564*, 565; **9**:665
in sand **9**:679
hemocyanin **3**:165
hemoglobin **1**:69; **9**:645
Hendricus, Jacobus **8**:608
henna **3**:196
Henry, Joseph **6**:434; **7**:485
Hercynian Mountains **8**:589
Herodotus **3**:180
heroin **1**:27
Héroult, Paul-Louis **1**:30
Herschel, Caroline **1**:46, 67;
3:209
Herschel, John F.W. **8**:604
Herschel, William **1**:46–47,
67; **3**:209, 218–219; **5**:370;
10:772
Hertz **9**:703
Hertz, Heinrich **3**:219–220;
9:659
Hertzsprung–Russell diagram
1:47
Hess, Victor **3**:166

Hewish, Antony **9**:647
hexacyanoferrate (III) **5**:375
hexamine chromium (II) **5**:375
hexane, immiscible with water
6:415
Himalaya Mountains **2**:113;
3:200; **4**:267, 318
Hiroshima **4**:*271*
Hiten (space probe) **6**:423
HIV (human
immunodeficiency virus)
1:73
hoarfrost **5**:*360*
Holland, John **6**:443
Holmes, Arthur **4**:305
Holocene epoch **2**:112; **9**:652
holography **5**:343–345, 398
hominids **2**:112
Honshu **10**:745
Hooke, Robert **3**:210; **7**:557;
10:750
Hooke's law **3**:210
Hoover Dam **2**:91
hormones **9**:645
Horsehead nebula **7**:523
horsetails **8**:589
hot spots **5**:381; **7**:515; **10**:781
hourglasses **10**:749
Huangdi, Chinese emperor
2:87
Huascaran, Mount **1**:63
Hubble Constant **5**:347
Hubble, Edwin **3**:169; **4**:291;
10:769
Hubble Space Telescope **3**:169;
4:*290*; **5**:346–347; **7**:519,
555; **8**:*624*; **9**:669; **10**:735
mirror **7**:554, 555
human immunodeficiency virus
(HIV) **1**:73
humans, early **1**:22; **2**:111;
4:283–284
Humboldt, Alexander von
4:302; **7**:485
humidity **1**:25; **5**:348–349; **7**:484
relative **5**:348–349; **7**:484, 486
humus **5**:325
Huron, Lake **5**:*392*
hurricanes **1**:49; **2**:*102*, 103;
4:273; **5**:350–351; **7**:*486*;
10:*790*
and storm surges **5**:351;
7:521
Hutton, James **5**:364, 394;
9:672
Huygens (space probe) **9**:683
Huygens, Christiaan **6**:405;
7:557; **9**:683; **10**:733, *750*

Hyatt, John W. **8**:619
hydrocarbons **2**:139;
5:352–353, 353; **8**:567
See also natural gas; organic
chemistry
hydrochloric acid **1**:10–11;
2:119
hydrocyanic acid **5**:355
hydroelectricity **3**:215; **4**:*244*
hydrogen **3**:235; **5**:354–355
in airships **3**:183; **5**:*354*
discovery **1**:10; **2**:123
and fusion **4**:288–289; **6**:450
ions **1**:10–11
is nonpolar **8**:*627*
isotopes **4**:288–289; **5**:354
liquid **3**:174; **5**:355
in the Universe **7**:532
hydrogenation, of fats **6**:412
hydrogen bonding **2**:92; **6**:414;
7:503; **10**:730
hydrogen chloride **7**:502;
8:*627*
hydrogen iodide **2**:118
hydrogen peroxide **5**:355
hydrogen sulfide **5**:355
hydrologic/water cycle *See*
water, cycle
hydrology **5**:356–357
See also groundwater
hydrometers **3**:183
hydronium ions **1**:11
hydrosphere **3**:201
hydrothermal vents **5**:358–359
hydroxides **8**:572
hygrometers **5**:349
hypersonic speeds **1**:17
hypotheses **8**:613

Iapetus (moon) **9**:683
Ibex rock series **7**:558
ice **5**:360–361
avalanches **1**:63
melting point **6**:*457*
See also glaciers
ice ages **1**:50; **2**:113, 133;
4:307, 310; **5**:362–365;
9:652
glaciers **5**:362, 363, 364, 367
and sea levels **2**:141, 158
ice caves **2**:110
ice cores **2**:133
Iceland **1**:48; **4**:*256*, 311; **5**:381
ice sheets **8**:581; **9**:652–653

ichthyosaurs **3**:173; **4**:*282*;
5:391; **6**:467
Ida (asteroid) **1**:43
ideal gas law **4**:293, 294; **8**:609,
637
igneous rocks **2**:128–129;
3:199–200; **5**:366–367;
9:672, 673
illite **2**:*127*
India **5**:369
Indian Ocean **5**:368–369
indicators **1**:11
Industrial Revolution, and coal
2:138
inertia **6**:450, 452; **7**:504, *512*
inflation **10**:770
Infrared Astronomical Satellite
(IRAS) **10**:735
infrared radiation **2**:144; **3**:*219*,
220; **5**:340, 370–371; **6**:404
discovery **1**:47; **3**:219; **5**:370
and the greenhouse effect
4:313
uses **5**:340, 371; **9**:668, 669
Infrared Space Observatory
9:669
infrasound **10**:764
inland seas **5**:372–373
See also Mediterranean Sea
instruments, musical **9**:703–704
insulators
electrical **3**:213, 215; **9**:701
heat **5**:339, 371
integrated circuits (silicon
chips; computer chips)
2:*125*; **3**:231
intensity, sound **9**:703
interference
light waves **5**:*344*;
6:405–406; **7**:554, 556
sound waves **1**:12–13; **9**:*703*,
705

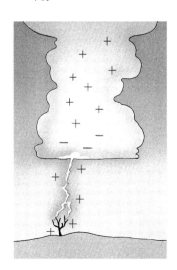

*The charges in a thunder
cloud and on the ground
when lightning strikes.*

interference fringes 6:*406*
International Space Station (ISS) 7:519; 9:710, *712*, 713
International Sun-Earth Explorers (ISEEs) 4:261
International Ultraviolet Explorer (IUE) 4:261; 10:735
interplanetary dust 6:477
Interplanetary Monitoring Platforms (IMPs) 4:261
interstitial solid solutions 1:28–29
intertropical convergence zone (ITCZ) 9:707; 10:761
intrusions 6:427
Inuit 8:629
Io (moon) 5:388, 389; 9:680, 698; 10:783
iodine 2:118; 5:*335*, 336, 337; 9:701
ion chambers 6:446
ion exchange 5:374
ionosphere 1:54; 5:**376–377**; 7:487; 9:658
ions 2:150–151; 5:**374–375**; 7:501; 9:677
    in the ionosphere 5:376
    polyatomic 2:151
Ireland, cliffs 2:128, 129
Irian Barat 1:60
iron and steel 5:**378–379**
    abundance of iron 8:564
    alloy steels 5:379
    carbon steel 1:29; 5:379
    cast iron 5:379
    Hadfield steel 6:437
    iron extraction 5:*379*; 6:472; 9:692–693
    iron ore in Australia 1:61
    magnetism 5:378–379; 6:434–436
    pig iron 5:379; 9:693
    reactivity of iron 6:470
    stainless steel 1:*28*, 29; 5:379
    steel 1:28, 29; 8:607; 9:*665*
    steel manufacture 5:379; 6:472–473
    wrought iron 5:379
    See also rust
ironstones, banded 1:54
irrigation 3:*194*, 195; 5:*332*; 10:785
islands 2:143; 5:**380–381**; 7:541; 10:780
isobars 5:350–351; 6:439; 7:485
isomers 5:353, **382–383**

isostatic recovery 5:363
isotherms 7:485
isotopes 3:235; 5:**384–385**; 7:526, 539; 8:593; 9:654
    carbon 2:97, 108; 5:384, 385; 9:654, 655, *656–657*
    cosmogenic 9:656–657
    hydrogen 4:288–289; 5:354
    nuclear spin 7:539
    plutonium 8:626
    and positron emission 3:226; 5:385; 9:655
    radioactive (radioisotopes) 5:385; 9:654
    tellurium 6:*471*
    uranium 3:235; 4:295; 5:384–385; 7:526; 9:656
isthmuses 2:142
Italy, floods 4:273
ITCZ (intertropical convergence zone) 9:707; 10:761

Jacks 6:*453*; 8:637
jade 4:300
Jamaica 2:102
Japan 4:273; 7:558; 8:577
Jeans, James 7:557
jet fighters, cockpit noise 1:14
jet streams 1:53; 5:**386–387**; 10:788
jetties 2:143
Jewish calendar 2:87
Johanson, Don 4:283
Johnstown, Pennsylvania, flood 4:273
Joint Global Flux Study 7:548
joints 5:367
Joule, James P. 3:174; 4:*248*; 5:*340*, 341; 8:611; 10:743
Joule–Kelvin Effect 10:743
joules 5:339
Joule–Thomson Effect 3:174
Juan de Fuca Ridge 3:171; 5:359
Jupiter 5:**388–389**; 9:697
    comet collisions with 2:149; 9:697
    day length 3:179
    Galileo probe to 1:43; 5:389; 7:*517*
    moons 1:45; 5:*388*, 389; 9:680, 698; 10:783

Pioneer probes to 8:*616*
    Voyager probes to 5:389; 10:783
Jurassic period 4:*284*; 5:**390–391**; 6:467

Kaiko (bathyscaphe) 6:444
kaolinite 2:*127*
Kara Strait 1:41
karats 4:317
Karnak, Temple of 1:44
karst landscapes 2:110; 6:*410*, 411
Kauai 10:789
Kazumura Cave 2:110
Kea, Mount 10:735
Kelvin, Lord *See* Thomson, William
Kelvin temperature scale 5:339–340, 341; 10:739, 743
    absolute zero 3:174; 4:*293*; 5:339–340; 10:743
Kennedy, John F. 1:35; 6:422; 7:518
Kennelly, Arthur 5:377
Kennelly–Heaviside layer 5:377
Kenya 1:22; 5:393
Kenya, Mount 1:19
Kepler, Johannes 1:45, 46; 3:169; 5:326; 7:527–528; 9:717
keratin 9:644
Kerch Strait 5:373
ketones 2:95
Kilauea volcano 2:110; 3:170
Kilby, Jack 3:231
Kilimanjaro, Mount 1:19, 21
kinetics 8:609
kinetic theory 5:341; 10:743
kinetic theory of gases 4:292–294
Kirchoff, Robert 9:715
Kivu, Lake 1:22
Klonk 3:188
Kobe, earthquake 3:207
Koobi Fara 1:22
Kosciusko, Mount 1:61; 7:544
Krakatoa, Mount 4:257; 10:744
Krebs cycle *See* citric acid cycle
Krebs, Hans 1:*71*
Kremer, Gerhard *See*

Mercator, Gerardus
krypton 4:*295*
Kuiper Belt 1:43; 8:625; 9:699

Labrador Current 1:50
Labrador Sea 1:50
Laccadive Islands 5:369
Lacertids 6:477
lactic acid, isomers 5:*382*, *383*
Laetoli 4:283–284
lagoons 2:143; 5:393
lakes 5:*329*, **392–393**
    in Africa 1:21–22
    and climate 2:131
    oxbow 5:392; 9:671
    salt lakes 1:61; 5:393
    See also inland seas
lamps
    fluorescent 6:419
    infrared heat 5:371
    ultraviolet "sun" 10:767
    See also lights, electric
Lanchester, Frederick 1:18
Land, Edwin L. 2:146
landfills 8:621; 10:757
landforms 5:**394–395**
La Niña 3:238
lanthanides 8:595
lapidaries 4:301
Laplace, Pierre-Simon 3:198
Large Electron–Positron Collider 8:586
lasers 2:145; 5:**396–398**; 7:556
    and holography 5:343–345, 398
    laser fusion 4:289
latex paints 8:579
latitude 6:439
    and climate 2:130
    horse latitudes 10:788, 796–797
lattices, crystal 9:701
Laurasia 1:19; 2:157; 4:318; 7:558; 8:582, *588*, 589
Laurentia 3:188
lava 3:170, *202*; 4:257; 5:366, 367; 7:514–*515*; 9:672; 10:*781*
    pillow 5:367; 6:427; 10:780
    See also magma
lava caves 2:*108*, 110
Lavoisier, Antoine 1:10, 30; 2:*123*–124; 5:341; 6:451; 8:573
Lavoisier, Marie 1:10, 30; 2:123–124; 6:451; 8:573
layer lattice, of clay 2:127
LCDs (liquid crystal displays) 6:*417*; 7:556

Volume numbers appear in **boldface type** followed by colons. Page numbers in **boldface type** refer to main articles and their illustrations. Page numbers in *italic type* refer to additional illustrations.

leaching **6**:473
lead **9**:665, 693
  extraction from ores **6**:473
lead azide **4**:262
lead iodide **2**:119
lead nitrate, reaction with
  potassium iodide **2**:119
lead sulfide **9**:693
Leakey, Louis, Mary and
  Richard **1**:22
Leavitt, Henrietta **1**:*47*
Leclanché, Georges **1**:65
  LEDs (light-emitting
  diodes) **3**:230; **4**:247
Lehmann, Otto **6**:416
Lemaître, Georges **3**:169
Lena River **1**:41
lenses **7**:*554*; **10**:733–734
Leonardo da Vinci **1**:18; **8**:603
Leonov, Alexei **9**:675
Lepaute, Nicole-Reine **2**:149
leptons **8**:585, 586; **10**:727
le Roy, Pierre **10**:751
Lesser Antilles **2**:102
levees **4**:272; **9**:671
Le Verrier, Urbain-Jean-
  Joseph **7**:525
levers **6**:*453, 454*, 455
Lewis, Gilbert Newton **1**:11
Libby, Willard **5**:*385*; **9**:657
Liberty Bell 7 (spacecraft)
  6:*464*, 465
lidocaine **1**:26
Liebig, Justus von **1**:69; **8**:567
life
  beginnings of **2**:88
  on Earth **3**:199; **6**:478
  on islands **5**:381
  simulating early conditions
  for **1**:72
life force, theory of **1**:69
lift **1**:16–17, 18
ligands **5**:375
light **2**:144; **3**:220; **6**:404–407;
  7:*552*–554
  brightness **6**:405
  and chemical reactions **6**:407
  colors in white light
  2:144–145; **3**:218; **7**:*528,
  529*, 553
  diffraction **6**:406; **7**:554, *556*
  and the Doppler effect **3**:193
  interference **5**:*344*;
  6:405–406; **7**:554, 556
  monochromatic **2**:145; **5**:396
  as particles **3**:227; **6**:405;
  7:553; **8**:602
  photoelectric effect **8**:602

polarized **3**:177; **5**:383; **6**:417
  red- and blue-shift **1**:67;
  3:193
  reflected **2**:145; **6**:405, *407*;
  7:*552*
  refraction **6**:406–407; **7**:495,
  553, 554
  and relativity **9**:666–667
  rotation by sugars **2**:96
  speed **3**:218; **6**:404, *405*, 407;
  7:*552*; **8**:611–612;
  9:666–667, 709
  ultraviolet *See* ultraviolet
  radiation
  and vision **7**:552–553, *555*
  wavelength **2**:144, 145;
  3:218; **6**:404, *405*; **7**:553;
  9:715
  wave–particle duality **6**:405;
  7:529, 553, 557
  as waves **3**:218; **6**:*405*; **7**:553,
  557
  See also color; holography;
  lasers; luminescence;
  mirages; optics; photons;
  rainbows
lightning and thunder **2**:137;
  6:408–409; **7**:531; **8**:617
  9:704; **10**:*789*, 790
lights
  electric **3**:214; **4**:*246*; **6**:406
  fluorescent **6**:419; **8**:617
  neon **4**:*295*
light-years **4**:290, 291; **7**:489
lignite **2**:140
lime *See* calcium oxide
limestone **1**:78; **2**:109–110;
  6:410–411, 469; **9**:673, 687
  caves **2**:108, *109*–110; **5**:331;
  6:411
  cliffs **2**:129
  Mississippian **7**:496
  pavements **6**:*410*
  uses **6**:411
limonite **9**:679
linseed oil **6**:412–413; **8**:578
lipase **3**:187
lipids **6**:412–413
Lipmann, Fritz **1**:71
Lippershey, Hans **10**:734
liquation **9**:665
liquid crystal displays (LCDs)
  6:*417*; **7**:556
liquid crystals **6**:416–417
liquids **4**:292; **6**:414–415, *451*;
  9:700
  capillary action **2**:92–93
  density **3**:183

diffusion in **3**:191
  See also evaporation and
  boiling; melting and
  boiling points
lithium **1**:57; **6**:468
lithium carbonate **6**:469
lithosphere **3**:201; **8**:622
litmus **1**:11
Lituya Bay **10**:745
Lockyer, Norman **5**:342
lodes **8**:564
lodestone **6**:432, 433
loess **4**:255
logging, and deforestation
  4:279
Lomonosov Ridge **1**:40–41
London forces **6**:415
London, Fritz **6**:415
longitude **3**:179; **6**:439;
  10:750–751
loudspeakers **4**:247; **9**:703
Love Canal **10**:757
Lovell, James **1**:38–39; **4**:299
Low Earth Orbit (LEO) **9**:681
Lubang Nasib Bagus **2**:108
Lumière, Auguste-Marie and
  Louis-Jean **8**:605
luminescence **6**:418–419, 469
luminol **6**:419
lunar missions **6**:420–423; **7**:510
  Apollo **1**:35–39; **4**:275;
  6:*422–423*; **7**:510, *511*, 518
  Lunar Orbiter program **6**:422;
  7:510
  Lunar Prospector (space probe)
  6:423; **7**:510
  lunar roving vehicle (LRV)
  1:39; **6**:*421*, 423
  Lunar Surveyor (space probe)
  6:423

Luna space missions
  6:420–421, 423; **9**:675
lungfish **3**:189
Lunik space missions **7**:510
Lunokhod (robot rover) **6**:423
luster, mineral **7**:490–491
Lycra **10**:731
Lyell, Charles **4**:304, 307
Lystrosaurus (reptile) **2**:157;
  10:759

Machines **6**:453–455
MACHOs **10**:771
Mackenzie River **1**:41
mackerel sky **2**:136
macromolecules **5**:374; **7**:*501*
Madagascar **5**:368
Maddox, Richard Leach **8**:604
Magellan (space probe)
  6:424–425; **9**:669
Magellan, Ferdinand **7**:544
Magellanic Clouds **4**:291;
  10:771
magenta dye **3**:197
magma **3**:170, 200; **5**:366–367;
  6:426–427; **9**:672; **10**:781
  acid **5**:367
  basic **5**:366–367
  and metamorphic rock
  6:474–475
  and ore formation **8**:564
  and the rock cycle **9**:673
  See also lava
magnesia (magnesium oxide)
  6:428
magnesite **6**:429
magnesium **6**:428–429, 469;

*The five time zones of the
lower 48 U.S. states.*

9:677
magnesium carbonate 6:429
magnesium oxide 6:429
magnesium sulfate 6:429
magnetic declination 6:430
magnetic inclination 6:430
magnetic poles 6:430–431; 8:581
  See also electromagnetism
magnetic resonance imaging
  (MRI) 3:224; 7:539
magnetic storms 6:435
magnetism 5:378–379;
  6:432–436; 9:701
  Earth's 1:58
  and electricity See
    electromagnetism
  paleomagnetism 8:581
  and polarity 8:627
magnetite 5:379; 6:431, 432;
  7:490; 8:581
magnetohydrodynamics
  (MHD) 6:436
magnetometers 6:446; 8:638
magnetosphere 6:431, 435
magnetrons 7:487
Majasaura (dinosaur) 6:466
malachite 2:121; 7:490
malaria 10:761
Malawi, Lake 1:22
Maldive Islands 5:369
mammals 2:112, 157; 3:173;
  4:265; 10:741
  evolution 6:467
mammoths 2:111, 113; 4:284;
  5:362; 8:597
manganate ion 6:437
manganese 6:437; 8:594
  nodules 5:369; 6:437; 8:565
  ores 6:437
  oxidation states 6:437; 8:571
manganese bronze 6:437
manganese dioxide 6:437;
  8:571
manganese (II) oxide 6:437
manganese (IV) oxide 6:437,
  470
manganese (II) sulfate 6:437,
  470
Manhattan Project 4:271
mannose 2:95
mantle, Earth's 3:199, 201, 202
  convection currents 3:202,
    203, 204
  upper 6:426
maps and mapping 4:302, 303;
  6:438–440
  ocean floor 6:440, 442, 443
  weather maps 5:387; 6:439

7:485
marble 1:78; 3:200; 6:475
Marconi, Guglielmo 5:377;
  9:659
margarines 6:412
Marianas 7:545
Mariana Trench 6:444; 7:541,
  545; 8:576
  discovery 7:547
Maricourt, Pierre de 6:432–3
marine exploration 6:441–444
Mariner probes 6:424,
  445–447; 10:776, 778
Marmara, Sea of 5:372, 373;
  6:456
Mars 3:198, 199; 6:447,
  448–449; 9:696
  atmosphere 6:448; 10:779
  distance from the Sun 9:697
  life on? 10:779
  Mariner probes to 6:445–6,
    447; 10:778
  Mars probes to 9:675
  meteorites from 6:449, 477
  moons 1:43; 6:449; 9:680
  surface 6:448–449; 9:696
  temperature 6:448; 10:779
  Viking probes to 6:448;
    10:778–779
Marshall Islands 7:545
Marshall, James 4:317; 7:494
marshes 10:792–793
Marsili, Luigi 6:442
marsupials 1:61
masers 7:487
mass 3:182; 5:327; 6:450
  relation to energy 4:271;
    6:450
mass spectrometers 8:567;
  9:657
mass wasting 4:255
matte 9:693
matter 6:451
  ancient Greeks and
    2:121–122; 6:451
  "dark" 6:451; 10:771
  shadow 4:276
  wave-particle duality 9:648,
    649
  See also atoms; gases; liquids;
    solids
Matterhorn 4:254; 7:514
Mauna Kea 7:515

Mauna Loa 3:170
Maury, Matthew Fontaine
  7:546
mauve dye 3:197
Maxwell, James Clerk 5:341;
  8:605
  and color photography 8:605
  and electromagnetism
    3:214–215, 219; 4:276;
    6:434; 7:557; 8:611
  and heat 5:341
Mayans, city of Chichén Itzá
  4:251
Mazama, Mount 3:170
McDivitt, James 4:297
McKinley, Mount 1:62; 7:533
Mead, Lake 2:91
meanders, river 4:253
mechanics 6:452–455
  See also gravity; momentum;
    motion
medicine
  isotopes in 5:384, 385
  See also surgery
medicines See drugs
  (medicinal)
Mediterranean climate 2:132
Mediterranean Sea 1:50;
  2:158; 5:372; 6:456
  in the Cenozoic 2:113
  formation 2:157; 10:741
Meitner, Lise 4:271
Mekong delta 3:181
Melanesia 7:544–555; 8:577
melting 8:606
melting and boiling points
  6:457
mendelevium 8:592, 595
Mendeleyev, Dmitri 1:57;
  2:125; 8:591–594, 626
meniscus 2:93
Mercalli scale 3:206
Mercator, Gerardus (Gerhard
  Kremer) 4:302, 303; 6:439,
  440
Mercator's projection 4:302;
  6:439
mercuric nitrate 6:459
mercurous chloride 6:458
Mercury (planet) 3:179, 198,
  199; 6:460–461; 9:695
  day length 6:460
  distance from the Sun 9:697

Mariner probe to 6:445–446,
  447
  temperature 6:447, 460;
    9:695
mercury (metal) 1:24;
  6:458–459, 473
  amalgams 1:29; 6:459
  in barometers 6:458
  in the environment 6:459
  poisoning 6:459
  to purify gold 4:317; 6:473
Mercury missions 1:36; 4:296;
  6:462–465; 7:518
mesomorphic state 6:416
mesons 4:276
  pi 8:585
Mesopotamians 1:44
  mapmaking 6:439
mesosaurs 8:582, 622–623
mesosphere 1:52, 53; 5:386
Mesozoic era 4:305; 6:466–467
  periods See Cretaceous
    period; Jurassic period;
    Triassic period
  Tethys Sea 4:257; 5:373
Messina, Strait of 7:495
metal detectors 6:470
metalloids 6:471
metallurgy 6:472–473
metals 6:468–470
  alkali 6:468–469
  alkaline earth 6:469
  atoms 3:177; 6:468; 7:501
  bonds 6:468; 7:501
  crystal structure 3:177
  extraction from ores 6:473;
    8:565
  mixtures See alloys
  pollution by 8:630
  post-transition 6:470
  reaction with acids 9:677
  reactivity series 6:470
  scrap 8:565; 9:665
  sheet 6:469
  transition 6:470; 8:594
  See also metallurgy
metamorphic rocks 2:129;
  3:200; 6:474–475; 7:490;
  9:673
metaquartzite 6:475
meteorites 3:171, 173, 198,
  203; 4:265; 5:378;
  6:476–477; 10:745
  age 4:305
  impact on Mercury 6:461
  from Mars 6:449, 477
  and metamorphic rock 6:475
  thermoluminescent 6:419

Volume numbers appear in **boldface type** followed by colons. Page numbers in **boldface type** refer to main articles and their illustrations. Page numbers in *italic type* refer to additional illustrations.

meteoroids **3**:170, 171; **6**:476, 477–478
meteorology **7:484–486**
  See also weather
meteors **3**:170–171; **6:476–478**
meteor streams **2**:149
methane **2**:*99*; **5**:352, 354–355; **7**:*503*
  atmospheric **2**:137
  burning **8**:573
  forming clouds **2**:137
  and global warming **4**:313, *314*
  in natural gas **7**:522
  and prospecting **8**:638
2-methylbutane **5**:382
methylpentene **5**:353
methylpropane **5**:382
Mexico City, earthquake **3**:*205*, 207
Mexico, Gulf of **10**:747
mica **5**:366; **9**:673
micelles **3**:*186*
Michelson, Albert **9**:709
Michigan, Lake **5**:*392*
micrite **6**:411
microgravity **9**:710, *711*; **10**:791
Micronesia **7**:545; **8**:577
microphones **4**:247; **9**:703
microprocessors **3**:231
  See also integrated circuits
microscopes **3**:*228*; **7**:*554*
  petrological **7**:491
microwaves **3**:220; **7**:*487*; **9**:669
Mid-Atlantic Ridge **1**:48; **3**:171, 206; **5**:359; **7**:515, 534
  discovery **6**:443
  formation **1**:49, **4**:257; **5**:381
midnight sun **7:488**
midocean ridges **3**:201; **5**:381; **6**:427
  aseismic **5**:369
  Atlantic *See* Mid-Atlantic Ridge
  faults **4**:266
  Indian Ocean **5**:369
  and ocean floor spreading **6**:431
  volcanoes **3**:171
Milankovitch, Milutin **5**:364–365
milk of magnesia **6**:429
Milky Way **1**:77; **4**:290, 291; **7**:489; **9**:*664*, *709*; **10**:769
Miller, Stanley **1**:72
Millikan, Robert **3**:227

mineralogy **4**:307; **7:490–491**
  See also crystals; gemstones
minerals **9**:673
  evaporite **8**:598–599
  hardness **4**:301
  thermoluminescent **6**:418–419
  See also prospecting
mining **7:492–494**
  alluvial **7**:493–494
  along fault zones **4**:267
  aluminum ore **1**:31
  in Antarctica **1**:34
  on asteroids **1**:43
  auger **2**:140
  coal **2**:139–140; **7**:*492*, 493
  copper **3**:165
  diamonds **4**:301
  gold **4**:317; **6**:473; **7**:493, *494*
  the oceans **6**:444; **7**:493
  open-pit bench **7**:493
  petroleum **5**:369
  strip **2**:140; **7**:493
  surface (quarrying) **7**:493
  underground **7**:494
  See also prospecting
Miocene epoch **2**:112; **10**:740
Mir (space station) **9**:713
mirages **7**:495, 554
Miranda (moon) **9**:698; **10**:*773*
mirrors **7**:553, 554
missiles
  aiming **3**:193
  heat-seeking **5**:371
  and the Star Wars program **5**:398
Mississippian period **2**:138; **7:496–497**; **8**:588
Mississippi River **9**:670, 687
  delta **3**:180, *181*
  floods **4**:272, 273
Missoula, Lake **2**:113
mists **5**:*348*, 349
mixtures **7:498–499**
  of liquids **6**:415; **7**:498–499
Mohammed **2**:87
Moho discontinuity **3**:201, 202
Mohorovicic, Andrija **3**:201, 202
Mohs, Friedrich **4**:301; **7**:491
Mohs' scale **4**:301; **7**:491
mole **1**:11
molecules **5**:374; **7:500–503**
  polar and nonpolar **7**:500–501; **8**:*627*
  See also isomers
Molina, Mario José **5**:337

molybdenum **8**:594
momentum **7:504–505**
monoglycerides **6**:413
monomers **7**:501; **8**:633
monosaccharides **2**:95
monotremes **1**:61
monsoons **5**:369, 387; **7:506–507**; **9**:685; **10**:761, 797
months, lunar **2**:84; **7**:508–509
montmorillonite **2**:*127*
Montreal Protocol **8**:575
Montserrat **2**:103
Moon **7:508–511**; **9**:695
  and calendars **2**:84–85
  craters **3**:171, 198; **7**:509, 510
  eclipse of **3**:200, 209; **7**:*509*
  far side **6**:420; **7**:510
  gravity **3**:199; **5**:327
  orbit **5**:*328*
  rainbows around **9**:661
  "seas" (maria) **7**:509–510, 511
  and tides **7**:509; **10**:746–747
  water on? **6**:423
  See also lunar missions
moonquakes **7**:511
moons **9**:680
Moorea **7**:*545*
moraines **4**:312; **5**:363, 392; **9**:653
mordants **3**:197
Morley, Edward **9**:709
morphine **1**:*26*, 27
Moseley, Henry **8**:593
mosquitoes **10**:*761*

Mossain, Henri **5**:336
motion **7:512–513**
  Newton's laws of **2**:114, 115; **4**:274, 277; **5**:327; **6**:452–453; **7**:504, 512–513
  relative **9**:666
  rotational **6**:455
motors **3**:224; **4**:247; **6**:434
mountains **3**:200; **7:514–515**
  and deserts **3**:184
  formation **2**:113; **4**:267, 318; **5**:395; **7**:514–*515*; **8**:623
  glaciers **4**:254
  metamorphic rocks **6**:475
  underwater **7**:515, 541
  and the weather **3**:184; **9**:*663*; **10**:790, 797
  See also midocean ridges; volcanoes
mudslides/mudflows **3**:195; **4**:255, 273; **10**:781
mudstones **2**:126; **7**:558; **8**:589
Müller, Franz **6**:*471*
Müller, Paul **5**:336
multiple mirror telescopes (MMTs) **10**:735
muons **3**:167; **8**:586
Murchison, Roderick **2**:89; **3**:188; **8**:598, *599*; **9**:689
Murdock, William **2**:139
Murray River **1**:61
Myanmar, oil wells **7**:550
mylonite **6**:475

A multivortex tornado.

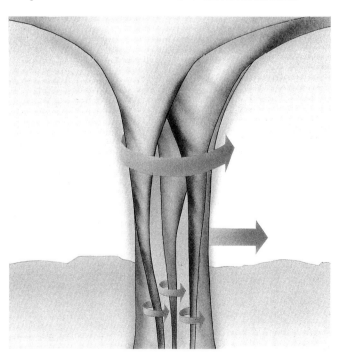

NACA **7:**516
Nagasaki **4:**271
Nakuru, Lake **1:**21
naphthalene **2:**139
NASA **7:**516–519
See also Apollo missions;
    Gemini missions; Hubble
    Space Telescope; Mercury
    missions; space probes
National Centers for
    Environmental Prediction
    (NCEP) **7:**521
National Earthquake
    Information Service **3:**206
National Weather Service
    (NWS) **5:**351; **7:**486,
    520–521
natural gas **2:**98; **5:**342; **7:**522,
    551; **8:**600
    under the oceans **1:***50*;
    5:369; **7:**493
nautiloids **7:**558
Nautilus (submarine) **4:**271
Navan **4:**267
navigation **6:**433, 442
NCEP (National Centers for
    Environmental Prediction)
    7:521
Neanderthals **2:**113; **9:**653
NEAR (Near-Earth Asteroid
    Rendezvous) **1:**43
nebulas **3:**169; **4:**291; **7:**523;
    9:*647*, 717, *717*
nematic crystals **6:**417
Neogene period **10:**740
neon **4:***295*
neon signs **5:**374
Neptune **7:**524–525; **9:**697, 698
    moons **7:**525; **8:**625; **9:***681*,
    698–699; **10:**783
    Voyager probe to **7:***524*, 525;
    9:*681*; **10:**783
Nereid (moon) **7:**525
neutralization reactions **1:**10
neutrinos **8:**586
neutrons **1:**57; **3:**234, 235;
    7:526, 539
    cosmic ray **3:**167
    discovery **7:**526, 539; **8:**584;
    10:726
    particles comprising **10:**727
neutron stars **1:**76; **5:**327;
    7:537; **9:**647, 718
    pulsars **9:**647
Nevado de Ruiz, Mount
    10:781
New Caledonia **7:**544
New Guinea **1:**60, 61; **7:**544

New Hebrides **7:**544
Newlands, John **8:**591
New Madrid, Missouri,
    earthquake **3:**207
Newtonian/classical physics
    7:527–529; **8:**609,
    610–611; **9:**648, 708
Newton, Isaac **7:**528; **8:**609
    and the apple **7:***529*
    and gravity **1:**46; **4:**251,
    274–275; **5:***326*–327;
    7:513, 528–529; **9:**708
    laws of motion **2:**114, 115;
    4:274, 277; **5:**327;
    6:452–453; **7:**504,
    512–513
    and light **2:**144; **6:**405;
    7:*528*, 529; **9:***660*, 661,
    715
    model of tides **10:**746–747
    telescope **7:***557*; **10:**734
New Zealand **2:***131*; **5:**381;
    7:544, 545
Next Generation Space
    Telescope (NGST) **5:**347;
    10:735
nickel **3:**165; **5:**378, 379
Niepce, Joseph-Nicéphore and
    Claude **8:**603
Niger River **1:**21
night vision binoculars **5:**340
Nile River **1:**21; **4:**272, 273;
    9:670
    delta **3:**180, *181*
Ninety East Ridge **5:**369
nitrates **5:**375; **9:**677
nitric acid **2:***104*; **7:**531
nitrides **7:**531
nitrogen **1:**52; **2:**124; **7:**530–531
    atmospheric **1:**52
    cycle **7:***531*
    and decompression sickness
    6:441–442
    fixation **7:**531
    liquid **3:**174, 175; **7:***530*
nitroglycerin **4:***262*–263
nitrous oxide, a greenhouse gas
    4:*313*
NOAA **7:**549
noble gases *See* gases,
    noble/inert
nodules **5:**369; **6:***437*; **8:**565,
    577

noise, measurement **1:**14
nonideal behavior **4:**294
nonmetals **7:**532
North America **7:**533–535
    during the Cambrian **2:***89*;
    8:581
    during the Silurian **9:**689
    ice ages **5:***365*; **9:**653
    time zones **10:***751*
North American Cordillera
    7:533, 535
North American Plate **7:**534
North Atlantic Current/Drift
    5:334
northeast passage **1:**41
northern lights *See* auroras
North Pole **7:**495
    and the north magnetic pole
    6:430–431
Northrop, John **2:**123
North Star *See* Polaris
Norway **2:**128, 129; **10:***736*
novas **1:**67; **7:**536–537
    supernovas **1:**76; **3:***166*, 167;
    4:261; **7:**536–537; **9:**718
Novocaine **1:**26
Noyce, Robert **3:**231
nuclear magnetic resonance
    (NMR) **7:**539
nuclear physics **7:**538–539; **8:**613
    See also fission, nuclear;
    fusion, nuclear
nuclear power **4:**271
nuclear wastes **10:**757
nucleases, restrictive **1:**73
nucleons **7:**539
nucleus, atomic **1:***56*; **3:**234,
    235; **7:**526
    discovery **1:**57; **3:**227–228;
    7:538–539; **10:**726
    forces in **4:**276–277; **8:**585;
    10:726–727
    See also neutrons; protons
nunataks **4:**311
nutation **4:**251
Nyasa, Lake **5:**393
nylon **1:**69; **8:**619–620, *632*,
    633; **10:**731

Oases **5:***333*
Oberon (moon) **10:***773*
obsidian **5:**366; **6:**427
occultation **3:**209

ocean currents **2:**143; **7:**541,
    542–543
    Atlantic Ocean **1:**49–50
    and climate **2:**131
    following **7:***548*
    Gulf Stream **6:**442
    Indian Ocean **5:**369
    in the ocean depths **1:**50
    Pacific Ocean **8:**576–577
    tidal **10:**747
    turbidity **2:**90, 91, 158
    upwellings **1:**50; **3:**236;
    7:541, *543*
    See also El Niño and La
    Niña; Gulf Stream
Ocean Drilling Project **5:***365*;
    7:*548*
ocean floor **2:**156; **3:***200*–201;
    7:540–541
    hydrothermal vents **5:**358–359
    magma **6:**427
    mapping **6:**440, 442, 443
    mining **6:**444; **7:**493
    spreading **6:**431; **8:**623
    submarine canyons **2:**90, 91,
    158; **6:**444
    See also midocean ridges;
    trenches, ocean
Oceania **1:**60; **7:**544–545
    See also Australasia
oceanography **7:**546–549
oceans **3:***200*–201; **7:**540–541
    and climate **2:**131
    life in the depths **6:**442–443
    mining **6:**444; **7:**493
    new oceans created **8:***623*
    pressure in **8:**637
    temperatures **7:***547*
    water **5:**356
    See also Atlantic Ocean;
    Indian Ocean; ocean floor;
    Pacific Ocean; sea level
Ogallala aquifer **5:**332
Ohio River, floodplains **4:**272
oil, crude (petroleum) **2:**98;
    7:530–531, 550–551; **8:**600
    formation **1:**54; **4:**283; **7:**522
    prospecting for **8:**638
    refining **2:**116; **8:**601
    spills **1:**70; **8:***631*
    under the oceans **1:***50*;
    2:158; **5:**369; **7:**493; **8:**638
oils *See* fats and oils
Old Faithful (geyser) **4:**309;
    5:331
Olduvai Gorge **1:**22
Oligocene epoch **2:**112;
    10:740, 741

Volume numbers appear in **boldface type** followed by colons. Page numbers in **boldface type** refer to main articles and their illustrations. Page numbers in *italic type* refer to additional illustrations.

Olympus Mons **6:**449
Ontario, Lake **5:***392*
ooliths **6:**410–411
Oort Cloud **2:**148; **9:**699
opals **1:**61; **4:**301
OPEC **7:**551
opiates **1:***27*
opium **1:***27*
optics **6:**404–405; **7:**529, **552–557**
    fiber optics **4:268–269**; **7:**556
Optiks (book) **7:***529*
Orbiter (space shuttle) **1:**17
Ordovician period **4:**264–265; **5:**364; **7:***558*
Oregon **5:**367; **7:**535
ores **8:564–565**
    dressing **9:**692
    metal extraction from **6:**473; **8:**565; **9:**692–693
    radioactive **8:**638
    See also prospecting
organic chemistry **2:**125, 139; **8:566–567**
    See also alkaloids;
        carbohydrates;
        hydrocarbons; lipids;
        plastics; proteins
organochlorines **5:**336
Orion Nebula **2:**155
Orsted, Hans Christian **1:**30; **3:**214, 222; **4:**276; **6:**433
oscilloscopes, cathode-ray **2:***106*, 107
osmosis **8:568–569**
Ostwald ammonia oxidation process **7:**531
Ostwald, Wilhelm **8:**608, 609
Ouachita Mountains **8:**588
ovens, microwave **3:**230; **7:***487*
overfishing, and coral reefs **2:**103
oxidation **8:570–571**, 572, 573
oxidation numbers **8:570–571**
oxides **8:**571, 572
oxygen **7:**532; **8:572–573**
    atmospheric **1:**52, 54; **8:**572, 581
    discovery **2:**123; **8:***573*
ozone **1:**53; **6:**407; **8:**572
ozone layer **1:**51, 53; **3:**199; **4:**313; **8:574–575**; **10:**724
    and CFCs **1:**53, 75; **5:**337
    holes **1:**33, 53; **6:**407; **8:**575; **10:**767

Pacemakers **1:**64
Pacific Ocean **8:576–577**
    El Niño and La Niña **3:236–238**; **8:**576, 577

hydrothermal vents **5:**359
Ring of Fire **3:**205; **4:**267; **8:**623
tidal waves **10:**744
trenches **7:***541*; **8:**576; **9:**707
    See also Mariana Trench;
        Oceania
pahoehoe **5:**367
Painted Desert **10:**759
paints **8:578–579**
    gloss **6:**413
    luminous **6:**469
    manufacture **6:**413
    See also dyes
Paleocene epoch **2:**112; **10:**740
Paleogene period **10:**740
paleomagnetism **8:**581
paleontology **4:**282, 307
Paleozoic era **4:**305; **6:**467; **8:580–581**
    See also under various periods of this era
Pallas (asteroid) **1:**42
Palm Sunday Tornado Outbreak **10:**755
pampas **5:**324; **10:**737
Panama, Isthmus of **2:**156; **9:**706
Pangaea **3:**172, 201; **4:**318; **8:**582, 589, 622
    break up **1:**19, 49; **3:**172; **4:**318; **5:**390; **8:**582; **9:**707; **10:**758–759
    climate **8:**599
    formation **4:**265; **7:**497; **8:**598
    supercontinents formed from
        See Gondwana; Laurasia
Panthalassa **8:**598
Papua New Guinea **1:***60*
parallax **1:**46; **9:**708, 716
particle accelerators **7:***538*; **8:585–**586; **10:**725, 727
particle physics **8:583–586**, 613
    antimatter **3:**226; **8:**584–585, 586; **10:**727
    discovery of electrons **1:**56; **2:**107; **3:**225; **8:**584; **10:**725
    discovery of neutrons **7:**526, 539; **8:**584; **10:**726
    discovery of protons **9:**646
    and fundamental forces **8:**585
    gauge bosons **8:**585, 586
    particle accelerators **7:***538*; **8:**585–586; **10:***725*, 727
    quarks **4:**277; **8:**586, 613; **10:**727
    standard model **8:**586

viewing particle tracks *See*
    bubble chambers; cloud
    chambers
    See also cosmic rays;
        subatomic structure
Pascal, Blaise **1:***25*
pascals **1:**25
pastes **7:**499
Patagonian Desert **3:**184
patina **3:**165
Pauling, Linus **7:***502*
PCBs (polychlorinated biphenyls) **1:**70; **8:**587; **10:**757
pearls **4:**300
Pearson, Allen **10:**755
peat **1:**54; **2:***139*, 140; **8:**589
pendulum **10:**749–750
peninsulas, coastal **2:**142
Pennsylvanian period **2:**138; **8:588–589**
pentaerythritol tetranitrate (PETN) **4:**263
pentane **5:**382
pepsin **2:**105
peptide bonds **1:**68; **9:**644
peridotite **6:**427
periodic table **1:**56, 57; **2:**125; **3:**234; **8:590–595**, 626
    See also elements
periods, geologic **4:***304*; **6:**466
periscopes **6:**407
Perkin, William **3:**196–197
permafrost **8:596–597**; **10:**763
permanganate **6:**437; **8:**571
permeability, magnetic **6:**435
Permian period **4:**265; **8:598–599**
Perseids **6:***476*, 477
Peru, rain forest destruction **4:**279
pesticides **1:**70; **5:**357; **8:**630
    spraying **3:**233

Peter the Pilgrim **6:**432–433
petrochemicals **8:600–601**, 632–633
petroleum ether **7:**499
petroleum *See* oil, crude
petrology **4:**307
PET scans **3:***226*
pH **1:**11
phase change **5:**341
phenol **8:**601
phenolphthalein **1:**11
Philippines, floods **4:**273
Phips, William **6:**443
phlogiston **2:**124; **8:**573
Phobos (moon) **1:**43; **6:***449*; **9:**680
Phoebe (moon) **9:**683
phonographs **9:**705
phosphates, in detergents **3:**187
phospholipids **6:**413
phosphor **2:**107
phosphorescence **6:**418–419
phosphorus **6:**419
phosphorus pentachloride **7:***503*
photocells **3:**215; **8:***602*
photoconductivity **8:**602
photoelectric effect **8:602**; **9:**649
photoemission **8:**602
photography **8:603–605**
    aerial **6:**440; **9:**668
    color **2:**147; **3:**197; **8:***605*
    developing film **6:**407
    digital **8:**605
    film **5:***337*
    flash **6:**428, *442*
    infrared **9:**668
    silver compounds used in **9:**691
    underwater **6:***442*

Earth's water cycle.

See also holography
photometers **2:**147
photons **2:**145; **6:**405; **7:**553; **8:**584, 602
   are carrier particles **8:**585, 586
   and chemical reactions **6:**407
   and lasers **5:**396, 397
   and luminescence **6:**418
photosynthesis **1:**54; **2:**94, 101; **8:**570, 571
   and carbon dioxide **1:**54; **2:**101
   and oxygen **8:**572
photovoltaic effect **8:**602
phthalic acid **6:**413
phthalocyanines **3:**197; **6:**437
physical change **8:606–607**
physical chemistry **2:**125; **8:608–609**
physics **8:610–613**
   geophysics **4:**307; **8:**612
   nuclear **7:538–539**; **8:**613
   space **9:**711
   See also Newtonian/classical physics; particle physics
Piazzi, Giuseppe **1:**43
Piccard, August **6:**444
Piccard, Jacques **6:**444
piezoelectricity **10:**765
pigments **3:**196; **8:***578*, *579*, 621
   See also dyes
pillow lava **6:**427
pi-mesons **8:**585
Pinatubo, Mount **4:**257
pingos **8:***597*; **10:**763
Pioneer program **8:614–616**
   Pioneer Venus missions **6:**424
pixels, LCD **6:**417
placer deposits **4:**317; **8:**564, 565
Planck, Max **7:**557; **9:**649
planetesimals **8:**625; **9:**699
planets
   day length **3:**179
   formation **9:**699
   and gravity **1:**46; **4:**274–275
   orbiting the Sun **1:**45, 46; **3:**169; **5:**326; **9:***697*
   See also Solar System
Planet X **8:**624; **9:**699
plankton **7:**522, 548
plants
   Cenozoic **2:**112
   Cretaceous **3:**173; **6:**467
   Devonian **3:**189

Jurassic **5:**391
Mississippian **7:**497
   and osmosis **8:**569
Paleozoic **8:**581
Permian **8:***598*, 599
Silurian **9:**689
   water transport **2:**93
plasma **4:**289; **8:617**
   and MHD generators **6:**436
   solar **10:***728*, 729
   See also solar wind
plaster of Paris **1:**78
plastic deformation **3:**210
plasticizers **8:**579, 621
plastics **7:**501; **8:618–621**
   degradeable **8:**621
   recycling **8:***621*
plate tectonics **2:**157; **3:***200*, *202*; **8:**582, **622–623**
   and the Atlantic Ocean **1:**48–49; **2:**102, 141, 157
   and Australasia **1:**60
   and the Caribbean **2:**102–103
   and coasts **2:**141
   and continental shelves **2:**158
   and earthquakes **3:**204
   and Eurasia **4:**256
   and faults **4:**267
   and Gondwana **4:**318
   and the Indian Ocean **5:**369
   and islands **5:**380–381
   and metamorphic rocks **6:**475
   and mountain-building **4:**267; **5:**395; **7:**514, *515*
   and the oceans **7:**540; **8:***623*
   in the Pacific Ocean **8:**577
   plate boundaries **8:**623
   and volcanoes **10:**780
platinum, catalysts of **2:**105
Plato **7:**556
Pleiades **2:**155
Pleistocene epoch **2:**112; **5:**392; **9:**652, 653
plesiosaurs **3:**173; **5:**391; **6:**467
Pliocene epoch **2:**112; **10:**740, 741
Plücker, Julius **2:**106
Pluto **5:**347; **7:**525; **8:**624–625; **9:**695, 697
   distance from the Sun **9:**697

plutonium **4:**271; **8:***595*, **626**; **10:**783
p-n junctions **9:**688
points, coastal **2:**142
poisons **1:**26; **5:**336
   mercury **6:**459
polar forces **6:**414
Polaris (Pole Star; North Star) **2:**154; **6:**430, 432; **9:***717*
polarity **7:**500–501; **8:**627
polar regions **8:628–629**
   climate **2:**130, 132; **10:**789
   daylight **3:**179
   deserts **3:**185
   glaciers **4:**311
   seasons **9:**684, 685
poles *See* magnetic poles; North Pole; South Pole
Pole Star *See* Polaris
pollution **1:**75; **8:630–631**
   air **3:**233; **8:**574–575, *630*, 631; **9:**693; **10:**724
   and bioremediation **1:**70
   by ozone **8:**574–575
   chlorinated pollutants **1:**70
   coastal **1:**70; **2:***142*
   control **8:**631
   detergents **3:**187
   from fertilizers **1:**75; **7:**531; **8:**631
   and global warming **2:**133; **4:**315
   light **8:**630
   and marine life **7:**548
   metal **8:**630
   noise **1:**13–14; **8:**630
   oil/petroleum spills **1:**70; **8:***631*
   PCBs **1:**70; **8:**587
   pesticides **5:**357; **8:**630
   soil **8:**631
   water **5:**333, 357, 393; **8:**631; **10:**785
   See also acid rain; toxic waste
polonium **9:**655
polyamides **8:**633
polychlorinated biphenyls *See* PCBs
polyesters **8:**620; **10:**731
polyethylene (polythene) **5:**352, 353; **8:**620, 632
polymers **6:**407; **7:**501; **8:632–633**; **10:**731

plastics **8:**619
polymerization **5:**353; **8:**633
See also proteins
Polynesia **7:***545*; **8:**577
polypeptides **9:**644, *645*
polyphosphazene **8:**633
polyps, coral **2:**103; **5:**395
polysaccharides **2:**96; **7:**501
polystyrene **8:**633
polyurethanes **8:**579; **10:**731
Population I and II stars **7:**489
positrons **3:**226; **5:**385; **7:**526; **8:**585; **9:**655; **10:**727
post-transition metals **6:**470
potassium **6:**468, 470; **8:**594, *608*; **9:**714–15
potassium fluoride **5:**337
potassium iodide **2:**119
potassium nitrate **6:**469
potassium permanganate **6:**437
powder, density **3:**183
Powell, John Wesley **2:**90; **10:**768
power plants **3:**215, 233; **4:**259
   cooling towers **4:**259
   nuclear **4:**270; **8:**626
   smokestacks **3:**233
prairies **5:**324
Prandtl, Ludwig **1:**17, 18
Pre-Archean eon **8:**634
Precambrian time **2:**88; **4:**305; **5:**364; **8:**580, **634–635**
precipitation *See* rain, sleet, and snow
pressure **1:**25; **8:636–637**
   of gases **4:**292–294; **8:636–637**
   See also air (atmospheric) pressure
Priestley, Joseph **2:**123, 124; **6:**458, 459; **7:**530; **8:***573*
Prime Meridian **6:**439
Principia Mathematica (book) **1:**46; **7:***527*, 528
printing **2:**146–147
prisms, and light **2:***144*; **3:**218; **5:**370; **6:**406–407; **7:***528*, 529, 553; **9:**661, 715
procaine **1:**26, 27
projections, mapmaking **4:**303; **6:***439*
Prontosil **3:**197
prospecting **8:638**
   for gold **6:**473; **7:**493, 494
protactinium **8:**595
proteins **1:**68–69; **7:**501, 502; **9:644–645**
   formation **1:**73; **8:**633
   See also enzymes

Volume numbers appear in **boldface type** followed by colons. Page numbers in **boldface type** refer to main articles and their illustrations. Page numbers in *italic type* refer to additional illustrations.

Proterozoic eon **8**:634
protium **5**:354
protons **1**:57; **3**:234, 235;
   7:538, 539; **9**:646
  cosmic ray **3**:167
  mass **9**:646
  particles comprising **8**:586;
    10:727
Proust, Joseph-Louis **1**:55
psoriasis **10**:767
pterosaurs **3**:173; **6**:467
PTFE (polytetrafluoroethene)
  5:337; **8**:620
Ptolemy, Claudius **1**:*45*; **2**:152;
  3:*168–169*; **4**:*302*
  mapmaking **6**:439
puddling furnace **5**:379
Pueblo Indians, caves **2**:111
Puerto Rico **2**:102
pulleys **6**:*455*
pulsars **9**:647
pumice **6**:427
PVC **8**:621
P waves **3**:204
pyroclastic flow **5**:367
pyrolusite **6**:437
pyroxenes **9**:673

Quanta **3**:227; **8**:612; **9**:648,
  649, 714
quantum chromodynamic
  (QCD) force **8**:585
quantum theory **7**:527; **8**:584;
  9:648–649
quantum mechanics **3**:228;
  8:609, 612
quarks **4**:277; **8**:586, 613;
  10:727
quartz **3**:*176*; **4**:300; **5**:366;
  9:650, 673
  clocks/watches **10**:751
  piezoelectricity **10**:765
quartzites **2**:129
quasars **1**:77; **4**:291; **9**:651;
  10:770
  and cosmic rays **3**:167
Quaternary period **2**:112;
  9:652–653
  epochs **2**:112
  ice age **2**:113; **5**:362, 364,
    392; **9**:652
quicklime (calcium oxide) **1**:78;
  6:411
quicksilver **6**:458

Radar **1**:47; **9**:*659*
  and depth of glaciers **5**:361
  Doppler **3**:192, 193; **9**:659

images of Venus **6**:424–*425*
imaging tornadoes **10**:755
police speed guns **3**:192, 193
and remote sensing **9**:*668–669*
and weather forecasts **3**:193;
  7:487, 521; **9**:659
radiation (electromagnetic) *See*
  electromagnetic spectrum
radiation (heat) **4**:247; **5**:341
radiation (ionizing)
  cosmic **3**:166–167
  detection **3**:166
radioactivity **4**:277; **7**:539;
  9:654–655, 656
  alpha decay **5**:385; **7**:526;
    9:654–655
  beta decay **5**:385; **7**:526;
    9:655
  carbon **2**:97
  and dating rocks **4**:305, 307;
    8:634
  detection **3**:166
  discovery **4**:270; **8**:*612*;
    9:655
  and gamma rays **3**:221;
    8:638; **9**:655
  and neutron capture **7**:526
  and nuclear waste **10**:757
  positron emission **3**:226;
    5:385; **7**:526; **9**:655
  See also fission, nuclear;
    isotopes; radiocarbon
    dating
radiocarbon dating **2**:108, 133;
  5:385; **8**:612; **9**:656–657
radioisotopes **5**:385, 385; **9**:654
radioisotope thermal
  generators (RTGs) **10**:783
radiometers **6**:446
radios **3**:229
  See also radio waves
radiotherapy **5**:*384*
radio waves **3**:219–220; **5**:377;
  9:658–659
  AM transmission **5**:377;
    9:658–659
  detection on Venus **6**:446
  FM transmission **9**:658–659
  and the ionosphere **5**:376,
    377; **9**:658
  nighttime radio **5**:*377*
  See also radar; telescopes,
    radio
radium **6**:469; **9**:655
radon **4**:295
rain, acid *See* acid rain
rainbows **2**:144, *145*; **6**:407;
  9:660–661

rain shadows **3**:184; **9**:*663*
rain, sleet, and snow
  (precipitation) **5**:356, 357;
    7:485; **9**:662–663; **10**:785,
    789–790
  and air pressure **1**:25
  and clouds **2**:134, 135, 136,
    137; **5**:356
  and humidity **5**:349
  monsoon rains **7**:*506*, 507
  raindrops **9**:663; **10**:730, 789
  and seasons **9**:685
  See also acid rain; drought
rainwater, and weathering
  9:687
ramps **6**:454–455
Ranger space program **6**:421–422
rare earth metals **8**:595
Rayleigh, Lord **7**:557
reactions, chemical
  See chemical reactions
reactivity series **6**:470
reactors **4**:271, 289
recording studios **1**:14
records (music) **9**:705
recycling **1**:*31*; **8**:565, *621*
  chemical **2**:120
red giants **1**:*66*; **7**:536, *537*;
  9:664, 718
redox reactions **8**:570, 571
Red Sea **1**:19
red-shift **1**:47, 67; **3**:193;
  9:651, 716; **10**:769
Redstone rockets **6**:464
reducing agents **8**:570
reefs, coral *See* coral reefs
refining **6**:473; **7**:551; **9**:665
reflection **6**:405; **7**:*552*
  reflecting telescopes **7**:*557*;
    10:733
  total internal **4**:268; **6**:406
refraction
  index of **4**:268
  law of **7**:557
  light **6**:406–407; **7**:495, *553*,
    554
  and mirages **7**:495
  and rainbows **9**:660–661
  refracting telescopes
    10:732–733, 734
  sound wave **9**:705
  total internal **6**:406–407
regolith **1**:43; **7**:510
reinforcement, acoustic **1**:12
relative atomic mass **5**:384

relativity **7**:527; **9**:666–667
  and electromagnetism **6**:434
  general theory of (theory of
    gravity) **4**:275–276; **5**:327,
    328; **8**:612; **9**:667
  special theory of **8**:611–612;
    9:666–667; **10**:752–753
remote sensing **9**:668–669
  satellites **5**:371; **9**:669
reptiles
  Cretaceous **3**:173
  Pennsylvanian **8**:589
  Permian **8**:599
reservoir rocks **7**:522
reservoirs **5**:393
resins
  alkyd **6**:413
  epoxy **1**:29; **8**:620
  in paints **8**:579
resistance, electrical **3**:213
resistors **3**:230
resonance **9**:704
respiration **2**:101; **8**:571
retina **2**:145–146; **7**:553
reverberations **1**:13, 14
reverberatory furnace **9**:693
rhyolite **6**:426, 427; **9**:672
rias **10**:775
ribonucleic acid *See* RNA
ribosomes **9**:645
rice paddies **4**:*314*
Richter, Charles **3**:206
Richter scale **3**:206
rickets **10**:767
Ridge Inter-Disciplinary
  Global Experiments **7**:548

Freefall conditions producing
weightlessness.

rift valleys **4**:266; **5**:393, 394–395; **10**:774
Rigel **2**:155
Ring of Fire **3**:205; **4**:267; **8**:623; **10**:780
Ritter, Johann Wilhelm **3**:219
rivers **9**:670–671
    in Africa **1**:21
    and canyons **2**:90–91
    deltas **2**:143; **3**:180–181; **9**:671
    deposition by **3**:180–181; **4**:253; **9**:671
    erosion by **4**:252, *253*; **9**:671
    floods **4**:272; **9**:671
    and lake formation **5**:392–393
    and landforms **5**:395; **10**:775
    river valleys **5**:395; **10**:775
    and sedimentary ores **8**:565
rivets, blind **4**:263
rivulets **4**:253
RNA (ribonucleic acid) **1**:73; **9**:645
Robinson's projection **4**:303
rock crystal **9**:650
rock pedestals **5**:395
rock phosphate **1**:78
rocks **9**:672–673
    dating **4**:304–305, 307; **6**:431; **8**:634; **9**:656
    Moon **6**:419, *423*
    See also geology; igneous rocks; metamorphic rocks; sedimentary rocks
rock salt **8**:598–599; **9**:687
rockslides **4**:255
Rocky Mountains **7**:535; **8**:589; **10**:740
    Chinook winds **10**:797
    coal beds **2**:138
    fossils **4**:285
Romans **2**:86, 87; **3**:164
Romer, Ole **6**:407
Röntgen, William **3**:177, 221; **10**:798
Roosevelt, Franklin D. **4**:271
rotational motion **6**:455
Rowland, F. Sherwood **5**:337
rubber **3**:211
rubidium **6**:468; **9**:715
rubies **4**:*300*, 301
Russia **5**:324; **8**:596; **10**:757
Russian space missions **9**:674–675
    race for the Moon **1**:36; **9**:675
    space stations **9**:674, 710, 712, 713

rust **2**:122; **5**:379; **8**:*570*, 571
Rutherford, Daniel **7**:530
Rutherford, Ernest **2**:107
    and atomic change **4**:270
    and the neutron **7**:539; **8**:584
    nuclear atom model **1**:57; **3**:227–228; **7**:538–539; **8**:584, 612; **10**:*726*
    and radioactivity **4**:307; **9**:655

Saami **8**:629
saccharides **2**:95–96
Sacramento, Gold Rush (1849) **4**:317; **7**:494; **8**:565
Sagittarius A* **7**:489
Sahara Desert **1**:22; **3**:184, 185; **5**:329
St. Helens, Mount **2**:133; **3**:*170*; **7**:515
salt domes **7**:*522*
salts **1**:10; **9**:676–677
salt *See* sodium chloride
Salyut missions (space stations) **9**:*674*, 710, 712, 713
San Andreas Fault **3**:205; **4**:266, *267*; **7**:534; **8**:623
sand **6**:471; **9**:678–679
sandbars **2**:143; **3**:180; **9**:679
sand-seas **3**:185
sandstone **3**:200; **6**:475; **7**:490; **8**:589; **9**:*679*, 687
    caves **2**:111
    quartz **7**:558
    Triassic **10**:759
San Francisco **3**:204–205, 207; **4**:267; **7**:494
Santa Ana Mountains **10**:797
sapphires **4**:301
Sarawak, caves **2**:108, 109
Sargasso Sea **1**:49
satellites **9**:680–681
    batteries in **1**:64
    Explorer probes **4**:260–261
    first **1**:35; **7**:516
    geostationary **9**:681
    infrared imaging from **5**:*370*, 371; **10**:735
    and mapmaking **6**:*440*, 443
    natural **9**:680
    remote-sensing **5**:371; **9**:669
    solar panels **1**:64

telescopes on **10**:735
    weather **2**:137; **5**:351, 371; **7**:*485*, 521, 547
Saturn **9**:682–683, 697
    day length **3**:179
    distance from the Sun **9**:697
    moons **9**:669, 680, 683, 698; **10**:783
    rings **9**:*683*, 697; **10**:783
    Voyager probes to **9**:682, *683*; **10**:783
Saturn V (rocket) **1**:36, 37; **6**:422
sauropods **3**:173; **5**:391
savanna **5**:324, *325*
SCADS **6**:444
scattering, light **7**:523
Scheele, Carl **2**:123; **5**:335; **6**:437; **7**:530
Schirra, Walter M., Jr. **6**:463, 465
schist **6**:475
Schmidt, Bernhard **10**:733
Schmidt, Maarten **9**:651
Schönbein, Christian **1**:65
Schrödinger, Erwin **3**:228; **9**:649
Schwarzschild radius **1**:77
scintillometers **8**:638
Scott, David **4**:298
Scott, Robert **1**:34
scuba equipment **6**:441–442, *443*; **7**:547
sea caves **2**:111; **4**:254
sea-floor spreading **6**:431; **8**:623
sea levels
    and global warming **2**:157; **4**:312, 315; **9**:652
    past **2**:141, 158; **8**:581
    and trade winds **3**:237
seamounts **5**:380; **7**:541
seas **7**:540
    inland *See* inland seas
sea scorpions **7**:558
seasons **2**:130; **3**:203; **4**:250; **9**:684–685
    See also midnight sun
sea stacks **4**:254
seat earths **8**:589
seawater
    drinking water from **6**:444; **8**:569

magnesium from **6**:428–429
    ships powered using **6**:436
    table salt from **6**:428–429
Sedgwick, Adam **2**:89; **3**:188; **4**:306
sedimentary rocks **2**:129; **3**:200; **5**:395; **9**:672–673, **686–687**
    fossils **4**:282
    See also limestone
sedimentation, of toxic waste **10**:756
sediments **3**:180, 181; **5**:395; **9**:686
    continental shelf **2**:158
sediment traps **4**:*285*
seesaws **6**:*454*
Segrè, Emilio **5**:336
seismic waves **3**:204, 206
seismographs **8**:638
seismology **9**:705
seismometers **3**:206
selenium **6**:471
semiconductors **9**:688
Semtex **4**:263
Sertürner, Friedrich **1**:27
Seychelles **5**:368; **10**:*760*
Seyfert galaxies **4**:291
Shackleton, Ernest **1**:34
shales **2**:126; **4**:284; **7**:558
sheet silicate **2**:127
Shepard, Alan B. **1**:35; **6**:463, 464, 465; **7**:518
ships
    floating **3**:*182*, 183
    friction **4**:287
    powered using seawater **6**:436
shipwrecks, discovery **6**:*443*
Shockley, William **3**:231
Shoemaker–Levy 9 comet **2**:149
Siberia, meteorite impact **6**:478
sidereal period **7**:508
Sidewinder missiles **5**:371
Sierra Nevada (United States) **7**:535
Sigma 7 (spacecraft) **6**:465
silencers **1**:13
Silent Spring (book) **5**:336
silica (silicon dioxide) **2**:126; **6**:426; **9**:679
    tiles **1**:17
silicates **7**:491; **9**:673
silicon **6**:471; **9**:679
silicon carbide **2**:99; **9**:679
silicones **8**:579, 620, 633

Volume numbers appear in **boldface type** followed by colons. Page numbers in **boldface type** refer to main articles and their illustrations. Page numbers in *italic type* refer to additional illustrations.

sills **5**:367; **6**:427, 474–475
Silurian period **3**:188; **9**:689
silver **3**:183, *217*; **9**:690–691, 693
silver azide **9**:691
silver bromide **5**:*337*; **9**:691
silver chloride **9**:691
silver cyanide **9**:691
silver iodide **3**:195; **9**:691
silver nitrate **9**:691
silver oxide **9**:691
silver sulfide **9**:691
singularities **1**:77
sink holes *See* swallow holes
sintering **3**:191; **9**:693
Sirius **2**:85
  system **1**:66; **10**:794
Skylab (space station) **7**:518; **9**:710, 712–713
skyscrapers, designed **3**:211
slack water **10**:747
slag **5**:379
slag heaps **10**:*757*
slaked lime (calcium hydroxide) **1**:78; **6**:469
slate **6**:475; **9**:650
Slayton, Donald K. **6**:463
slingshot, gravitational **10**:782
sluice boxes **7**:493
smelting **6**:473; **8**:565; **9**:692–693
Smith, William **4**:*305*, 306; **8**:588
smogs **7**:531; **8**:574, 631
smoke, diffusion **3**:*190*
smoke alarms **3**:230
Snake River **2**:91; **2**:113
Snell's law **7**:557
Snell, Willebrord **7**:557
snow **5**:361; **9**:*662*, 663; **10**:790
  avalanches **1**:*62*–63
snowstorms, lake-effect **2**:131
soaps **3**:186; **6**:*412*, 413
  See also detergents
Society Islands **7**:*545*
sodium **2**:150; **6**:468
  reaction with chlorine **2**:118–119; **5**:374–375; **8**:571
sodium azide **4**:263
sodium bicarbonate **6**:468–469
sodium carbonate
  hydrated **6**:468
  reaction with acetic acid **1**:*10*
  reaction with hydrochloric acid **2**:119
sodium chloride (salt) **2**:119, 150–*151*; **3**:177; **8**:571; **9**:*676*

crystals **9**:*677*, *700*
  dissolving in water **8**:607, 627
  electrolysis **3**:216–217
  from seawater **7**:493
  ionic lattice **2**:*151*; **5**:*375*
sodium hydroxide **3**:216; **6**:468
  reaction with sulfuric acid **1**:10; **2**:117, 118
sodium nitrate **4**:263
sodium sulfate **2**:117, 151
soil
  erosion **3**:195; **4**:255
  pollution in **8**:631
soil creep **4**:255
solar constant **5**:341
solar panels **1**:64
  on space probes **6**:446
Solar System **1**:52; **3**:198; **7**:489; **9**:694–699
  See also asteroids; comets; meteors; planets; Sun
solar wind **5**:376; **8**:617; **9**:695; **10**:728
  and auroras **1**:59; **6**:431, 435
  spectrometers to measure **6**:446
solders **1**:29
solenoids **6**:436
solidification **8**:606
solids **4**:292; **6**:*451*; **9**:700–701
  diffusion in **3**:191
  ionic **5**:374
  melting points **6**:457; **9**:*701*
Solomon Islands **7**:544
solstices *See* equinoxes and solstices
solutions **6**:415; **7**:*498*; **8**:607
  solid **8**:607
solvent extraction **7**:499
sonar **3**:192; **6**:443; **9**:*705*; **10**:765
sonic boom **9**:*704*
soot **8**:573
Sorensen, Soren **1**:11
Sosigenes **2**:86
sound **9**:702–705
  and the Doppler effect **3**:*192*
  infrasound **10**:764
  and light **6**:419
  recording **9**:705
  speed **6**:409; **9**:704
  used for prospecting **8**:638
  waves **1**:12–13; **8**:638; **9**:702, *703*, 704–705
  See also acoustics; ultrasound
sound chambers **1**:*13*
sound-level meters **1**:14

South Africa, diamonds **4**:301
South America **5**:324; **9**:706–707
  joined to Africa **8**:622
southern lights *See* auroras
Southern Ocean **7**:540
South Pole **1**:32
  mirages at **7**:495
  and the south magnetic pole **6**:431
Soxhlet apparatus **7**:499
Soyuz spacecraft **1**:36; **9**:*674*
space **9**:708–709
spacecraft, launched **3**:*174*, 175
space heaters **5**:*339*
space race **1**:35; **6**:462
space science **9**:710–711
  See also weightlessness
space shuttles **7**:*518–519*
space sickness **9**:711
space stations **5**:328; **7**:518, 519; **9**:712–713
  and gravity **5**:328
  See also International Space Station; Salyut missions; *Skylab*
Space Telescope Science Institute **5**:346
space-time continuum **9**:709; **10**:753
space walks **4**:297, 298, *299*; **9**:675
spandex fibers **10**:731
specific gravity, of minerals **7**:491; **9**:673
specific heat capacity **5**:340
spectrographs **9**:715
spectrometers **9**:*714*, 715
  mass **8**:567; **9**:657
  solar plasma **6**:446
spectroscopy **9**:649, **714–715**
spectrum, light **2**:*144*; **3**:218; **7**:553; **9**:661, *715*
speed **7**:513
spin, nuclear **7**:539
Spindletop oil field **7**:551
spinnerets **10**:731
spits, coastal **2**:143
Spitzer, Lyman **5**:347
spontaneous emission **5**:397
sport, aerodynamics of **1**:18
springs **5**:330
  hot *See* geysers
Sputnik 1 (satellite) **4**:260
Sputnik missions (satellites) **4**:260; **7**:516; **9**:*674*, *681*

Sri Lanka **5**:368, 380
Stafford, Thomas **4**:298
Stahl, Georg Ernst **2**:124; **8**:573
stalactites and stalagmites **2**:*101*, 108, 110; **5**:331
starches **2**:94, 96; **8**:633
starfish, fossil **7**:*558*
Starr, J.W. **6**:406
stars **9**:716–718
  becoming black holes **1**:76–77
  binary (double) **1**:66–67; **3**:209; **7**:536; **9**:716–717; **10**:794
  blue **7**:489, *537*; **9**:716, 717, 718
  brightness **1**:47, 67; **2**:153; **9**:717
  distances **1**:46, 47
  eclipsed **3**:209
  elements from **3**:*234*, 235
  failed **5**:388
  formation **9**:717; **10**:770
  mass **1**:67; **9**:717
  moving relative to Earth **1**:67; **3**:193
  neutron *See* neutron stars
  nuclear fusion in **5**:327
  optical doubles **1**:66, 67
  Population I and II **7**:489
  red **9**:716, 717
  red giants **1**:*66*; **7**:536, *537*; **9**:*664*, 718
  shooting *See* meteors
  white dwarfs **1**:67, 76; **7**:523, *536*, 537; **9**:718; **10**:794
  yellow **9**:716, 718
  See also constellations; galaxies; novas; pulsars; Sun
Star Wars program **5**:*398*
state, change of **8**:*606*
stratopause **10**:724
Statue of Liberty **3**:*165*
steam reforming **5**:355
steel *See* iron and steel
steppes **5**:324
stereoisomerism **5**:383

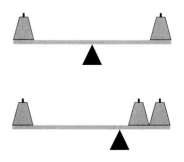

Two seesaws with the fulcrum in different positions.

stimulated emission **5:**396, 397
Stonehenge **1:**44; **2:**85
storage heaters, night **4:**245
storm surges **5:**351; **7:**521
Strabo **4:**302
strain **3:**211
straits **5:**372
Strassmann, Fritz **4:**270–271
strata **8:**564; **9:**673, 686
Strategic Defense Initiative
   (SDI) **5:***398*
stratigraphy **4:**307
stratosphere **1:***52*, 53; **5:**386;
   10:724
   See also ozone layer
streak, mineral **7:**490
streamers **6:**409
stress **3:**210–211
stromatolites **8:***635*
strong nuclear force **3:**235;
   4:276–277; **8:**585; **9:**646
   carrier particles for **8:**585
strontium **6:**469
Sturgeon, William **3:**224;
   6:434
styrene **8:**601
styrofoam **8:**632
subarctic region **2:**132
subatomic structure **1:**56–57;
   7:539; **10:725–727**
   Bohr model **3:**228; **8:**584;
     9:649; **10:**726
   discovery of electrons **1:**56;
     2:107; **3:**225; **8:**584;
     10:*725*
   discovery of neutrons **7:**526,
     539; **8:**584; **10:**726
   discovery of the nucleus
     1:57; **3:**227–228;
     7:538–539; **10:**726
   discovery of protons **9:**646
   nuclear atom model **1:**57;
     3:227–228; **7:**538–539;
     8:584, 612; **10:**726
   "plum pudding" model **1:**56;
     2:107; **7:**538; **8:**584;
     10:*725*
   quarks **4:**277; **8:**586, 613;
     10:727
   subatomic forces **4:**276–277;
     8:585; **10:**726–727
   See also particle physics
subduction **2:**158; **4:**257, 267;
   6:427; **8:**623
sublimation **2:**100; **5:**361;
   8:606; **9:***701*
submarines **4:**271; **6:**443–444;
   8:637

nuclear-powered **4:**271
submersibles **6:**443–*444*; **7:***548,*
   549
subtropics **2:**132
   deserts **3:**184
sucrose **2:***96*
Sudan, floods **4:**273
Suess, Eduard **5:**373
sugar(s) **2:***94–96*; **3:***191*; **9:***700*
sulfates **5:**375; **9:**677
sulfides **7:**491; **8:**638
sulfur, removal from fuels
   8:601
sulfur bacteria **8:**577
sulfur dioxide **5:**357; **8:**631;
   9:693
sulfur hexafluoride **7:***503*
sulfuric acid **8:**572
   and acid rain **5:**357; **9:**693
   reaction with sodium
     hydroxide **1:**10; **2:**117, 118
sulfur trioxide **8:**572
Sumatra **5:**369
Sumner, James **1:**71; **2:**123
Sun **9:**694–695; **10:728–729**
   bending light **9:**667
   and calendars **2:***84*, 85
   energy from **4:**245; **5:**341
   formation **9:***696*
   helium **5:**342
   magnetic field **6:***435*
   nuclear fusion **4:***288*; **6:**450;
     9:694; **10:**729
   rainbows around **9:**661
   sunlight and climate **2:**130–131
   sunspots **6:**435; **10:**728, *729*
   See also midnight sun; solar
     wind; stars
Sunda Trench **5:**369
sundials **2:***84*; **10:**748–749
superclusters, galaxy **4:**290,
   291
supercomputers, and weather
   forecasts **7:**486
superconductors **3:**175; **10:**739
superfluidity **3:**175
Superior, Lake **5:***392*
supernovas **1:**76; **4:**261;
   7:536–537; **9:**647, 718
   and cosmic rays **3:***166*, 167
supersonic speeds **1:**15, 17;
   9:*704*
superstring theory **4:**276

supertwists **6:**417
surface tension **2:**92–93; **3:**186;
   10:730
   and capillary action **2:**93
   and surfactants **3:**186
surgery
   keyhole **4:***267*
   laser **5:**398
Surveyor program **6:**422; **7:**510
   Surveyor 3 **1:**38; **6:**422, 423
Sutter, James Augustus **4:**317
Sutter, John **7:**494
Suwarrow **5:**381
Svedberg, Theodor **1:**69
swallow holes (sink holes;
   dolines) **2:***109*, 110
swamps **10:**792, *793*
Swan, Joseph Wilson **3:**214;
   6:406
S waves **3:**204
Swigert, John **1:**38–39
swings, energy **4:***247*
symbols, chemical **2:**117
symmetry, crystal **3:**176, *177*
synclines **7:**515
synodic period **7:**508
synthetic aperture radar (SAR)
   6:424–425
synthetic fibers **10:731**

Table Mountain **7:**514
Tahiti **7:***545*
Tahoe, Lake **5:**393
taiga **4:**279; **10:**762
tailwinds **5:**386
Talbot, William Henry Fox
   8:604
talc, hardness **7:**491
Tambora, Mount **2:**133; **4:**257
Tanganyika, Lake **1:**21–22;
   5:393
Tanzania **1:**22; **5:**393
tar **7:**550
tartrazine **3:**197
tau particles **8:**586
Tavurvur, Mount **1:***60*
TCDD **5:**336
technetium **3:**235
tectonic plates *See* plate
   tectonics
Teflon **5:**337; **8:***619*, 620
Tektite II (underwater project)
   7:549

telescopes **7:**557; **10:732–735**
   cosmic ray **3:**167
   first **1:**45; **7:**557; **10:***734*
   Galilean **10:**733, *734*
   infrared **5:**371; **10:**735
   radio **9:***658*; **10:**732, 734–735
   reflecting **7:**557; **10:**733
   refracting **10:**732–733, *734*
   relector-refractor **10:**733
   See also Hubble Space
     Telescope
televisions **2:**106, *107*, 147
   cathode-ray tubes **2:**106, *107*
   screens **6:**419
tellurium **6:***471*; **8:**593
temperate regions **2:**132;
   10:736–737
   forests **4:**280; **10:**737
   grasslands **5:**325; **10:**737
   seasons **9:***684*, 685; **10:**736
temperature(s) **5:**338;
   10:738–739
   absolute zero **3:**174; **4:**293
   atmospheric **7:**484
   cryogenic **3:**174–175
   lowest on Earth **1:**33
   measuring **5:**339–340, 341
   scales **5:**339, 341; **10:**738,
     739
   See also heat
Tereshkova, Valentina **9:**674,
   675
Tertiary period **2:**112, 113;
   10:740–741
Terylene **10:**731
Tesla, Nikolai **3:**224
Tethys Sea **2:**157; **4:**257;
   5:373, 390; **8:**598; **10:**741
tetrachloromethane **6:**415
Thales of Miletus **2:**121; **3:**233
theodolites **6:**440; **10:**796
theories of everything (TOEs)
   4:276
thermal conductivity **5:**339
thermodynamics **4:**248; **8:**609,
   611; **10:742–743**
thermograms **5:***338*, 371
thermoluminescence **6:**418–419
thermometers **5:**341; **10:**739
thermoplastics **8:**620
thermosets **8:**620
thermosphere **1:***52*, 53–54;
   5:386
Thompson, Benjamin (Count
   Rumford) **5:**341
Thomson, J. J. **1:**56; **2:**107;
   3:215, *225*–227; **7:**538;
   8:584, 612; **10:**725

Volume numbers appear in **boldface type** followed by
colons. Page numbers in **boldface type** refer to main
articles and their illustrations. Page numbers in *italic type*
refer to additional illustrations.

Thomson, William (Lord Kelvin) **3**:174; **4**:305; **5**:341; **10**:*743*

thorium **8**:595, 638

Three Mile Island **4**:271

thrust **1**:17

thunder *See* lightning and thunder

thunderstorms **2**:135; **6**:408

thymine **1**:71–72

Tibesti Mountains **1**:20

tidal waves (tsunamis) **3**:173, 205; **4**:273; **10**:**744–745**, 781, 787

tides **7**:509; **10**:**746–747**
  and coastal erosion **2**:142
  spring and neap **10**:747

tiles, silica **1**:17

tillites **5**:363–364

timbre **9**:703

time **10**:**748–751**
  atomic **3**:179
  dilation **10**:753
  geologic **4**:304–305, 306–307
  solar **3**:179

time travel **10**:**752–753**

time zones **3**:*178*, 179; **10**:*751*

tin **5**:379; **9**:665

tintypes **8**:604

tires, friction **4**:287

TIROS 1 (satellite) **2**:137; **7**:*485*, 521

Titan (moon) **9**:669, 680, 683, 698; **10**:783

Titan II rockets **4**:296, 297, 299

Titania (moon) **10**:*773*

titanium **8**:594

titanosaurs **5**:*390*

Titicaca, Lake **9**:707

tokamaks **4**:289

toluene **2**:139; **8**:601

Tombaugh, Clyde **8**:*625*

topaz **4**:300, *301*

tornadoes **3**:193; **7**:*520*, 521; **10**:**754–755**, 790

Torricelli, Evangelista **1**:24

torus **4**:289

Toubkal, Jebel **1**:20

tourism, and coral reefs **2**:*103*

toxic waste **10**:**756–757**
  and cryogenics **3**:175

trade winds *See* winds, trade

trains **1**:15; **4**:287
  maglev **6**:*436*

Transantarctic Mountains **1**:33

transducers **4**:247

transformers **3**:215, 224

transient lunar phenomena (TLPs) **7**:511

trans- isomers **5**:383

transistors **3**:230, 231; **9**:688

transition metals **6**:470; **8**:594

translucency **6**:405

transparency **6**:405

transuranic elements **3**:235; **8**:626

travertine **6**:411

tree rings, and radiocarbon dating **9**:*656*, 657

trees, deciduous **10**:761

trenches, ocean **3**:201, 203; **4**:267; **7**:*541*, 545; **8**:623; **10**:774

triangulation **6**:440

Triassic period **6**:467; **10**:**758–759**

trichloromethane **6**:414

triglycerides **6**:412

trilobites **2**:*88*–89; **6**:467; **7**:558; **9**:689

Trinidad and Tobago **2**:102

trinitrotoluene (TNT) **4**:263

triodes **3**:231

tritium **5**:354

Triton (moon) **7**:525; **8**:625; **9**:*681*, 698–689; **10**:783

Trojans (asteroids) **1**:43; **9**:696

tropical regions **2**:132; **4**:280; **5**:324; **9**:685; **10**:**760–761**, 788
  See also monsoons; winds, trade

tropopause **10**:724, 796, 797

troposphere **1**:*52*, 53; **2**:134; **5**:386; **10**:724

tsunamis *See* tidal waves

tuff **4**:284; **5**:366
  welded **5**:367

tundra **1**:74; **2**:132; **8**:*597*; **10**:**762–763**

Tunguska, Siberia **2**:149

turbines **10**:742, 765

turpentine **8**:578

turquoise **4**:300

typhoons **4**:273; **5**:350

Tyrrhenian Sea **6**:456

Ultrasound **10**:**764–765**
  uses **3**:193; **9**:705; **10**:*764*, 765

ultraviolet radiation **2**:144; **3**:219, *220–221*; **6**:404; **10**:**766–767**
  and fluorescence **3**:219
  and free radicals **5**:375

and ozone **1**:52, 53; **6**:407; **8**:575; **9**:669; **10**:767
  uses **10**:767

Umbriel (moon) **10**:*773*

uncertainty principle **9**:649

Union Carbide factory disaster **8**:601

United States
  earthquakes **3**:*207*
  floods **4**:272–273
  ice ages **5**:*365*
  tornadoes **10**:755

United States Geological Survey (USGS) **10**:768

universal gravitation, law of **4**:275; **5**:326–327; **7**:513, 528–529

Universe **10**:**769–771**
  beginning *See* Big Bang
  "dark matter" **6**:451; **10**:771
  expanding **1**:47; **3**:169, 193; **4**:291; **5**:347; **10**:769–771
  infinite number **10**:753
  shape **10**:771
  study of *See* cosmology

updrafts **10**:795

upwellings **1**:50; **3**:236; **7**:541, *543*

Ural Mountains **4**:257; **8**:599

uranium **8**:595, 638
  enriched **4**:295; **5**:384–385
  isotopes **3**:235; **4**:295; **5**:384–385; **7**:526; **9**:656
  nuclear fission **4**:270–271

uranium hexafluoride **4**:295; **5**:337, 384–385

Uranus **1**:46; **3**:209; **7**:525; **9**:697–698; **10**:**772–773**
  Voyager probe to **3**:209; **10**:772, 773, 783

urea **1**:69

urease **1**:71

Urey, Harold **1**:72

Uruguay **9**:707

USGS (United States Geological Survey) **10**:768

Vacuums **5**:339

vacuum tubes **3**:231

Vaiont Dam **4**:273

valence **8**:591–592
  valence shells **7**:501–502; **8**:592

valleys **10**:**774–775**
  formed by glaciers **4**:*306*, 307; **9**:*652*; **10**:775
  hanging **4**:254; **10**:775
  rift **4**:266; **5**:393, 394–395; **10**:774
  U-shaped **4**:254; **5**:363, 395; **10**:762, 774, 775
  V-shaped **4**:253; **5**:394, 395; **10**:774
  See also canyons; trenches, ocean

vanadium **8**:594

Van Allen belts **4**:260; **8**:617

Van Allen, James **4**:260

Van de Graaff generators **3**:*233*

Van de Graaff, Robert **3**:233

van der Waals forces **7**:502

Vanguard rockets **4**:260; **7**:516

vapor pressure **4**:258, 259; **5**:349

vapor(s) **4**:*294*
  water **1**:25, 52; **5**:348, 349; **7**:*500*

vectors **7**:*513*

Vega (star) **2**:155; **4**:251

vegetation
  and altitude **2**:*131*; **4**:278
  See also forests; plants

veld **5**:324; **10**:737

velocity **7**:513

Venera probes **6**:424; **9**:675; **10**:777

Venezuela, floods **4**:273

Venus **3**:198, 199; **6**:424, 425, 447 **9**:695; **10**:**776–777**
  day length **3**:179; **10**:776

Layers of rock are broken and pulled out of line at a fault.

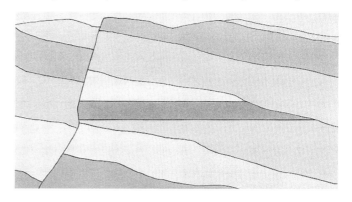

distance from the Sun **9:**697; **10:**776

Magellan probe to **6:**424–425

Mariner probes to **6:**424, 445–447; **10:**776

Pioneer missions to **6:**424; **8:***614*, 616

surface **6:**425; **10:**777

temperature **6:**424, 446, 447; **10:**776

Venera missions to **6:**424; **9:**675; **10:**777

Venus Orbiting Imaging Radar (VOIR) **6:**424

Verne, Jules **6:**441

Very Large Array (VLA) **10:**735

Victoria, Lake **1:**21

Viking probes **6:***448*; **10:778–779**

vinblastine **1:**26

Vinci, Leonardo da **1:**18; **8:**603

vincristine **1:**26

Vine, Allyn **6:**444

Virgin Islands **2:**102

virtual reality **9:***708*

viscose **10:***731*

viscosity **4:**287

vision **2:**145–146; **7:**552–553, *555*

vitamins, and free radicals **5:**375

voids **4:**291

volcanoes **10:780–781**

and climate **2:**133

craters **3:***170*

during the Cretaceous **4:**265

of Eurasia **4:**257

formation **3:**203; **7:**514–*515*; **8:**623; **10:***781*

forming islands **5:**381; **7:**515; **10:**780

lava **3:***202*; **5:**367; **7:**514–*515*

and magmas **6:**426, 427

Tertiary period **10:***741*

tunnels and caves **2:**110

underwater **3:**171; **5:**381; **7:**515, 534; **10:**781

See also Ring of Fire

Volta, Alessandro **1:**65; **3:**214, 215; **6:**433

voltaic pile **1:**65; **3:**214, 215

Vostok spacecraft **9:**674, 675

Voyager Interstellar Mission **10:**783

Voyager probes **3:**209; **5:**389; **7:***524*, 525; **9:***681*, 682, *683*; **10:**772, 773, 782–783

Waals, Johannes van der **7:**502

wadis **4:**254; **9:**670; **10:***775*

Walcott, Charles Doolittle **2:**89

Walsh, Don **6:**444

Washington, basalts **5:**367

water **10:784–785**

boiling point **4:**258, *259*; **6:**457; **8:***606*; **10:**784

conservation **5:**332–333

cycle **3:**194; **5:**329, 356, *357*; **7:**540; **9:**662; **10:**784–*785*, 789

on Earth **3:**199, 200

formation **8:**571

freezing point **5:**361

from forests **4:**280

hard **3:**186; **5:**374; **9:**677

and life **3:**199

molecules **2:**92; **7:**503

pH **1:**11

pollution **5:**333, 357, 393; **8:**631; **10:**785

a solvent **6:**415

specific heat capacity **5:**340

states **6:**457; **8:***606*, *607*; **10:**784

surface **5:**357

surface tension **10:**730

underground *See* groundwater

vapor *See* vapor(s), water

See also glaciers; humidity; hydrology; ice; lakes; oceans; rivers

waterfalls **4:**252; **9:**671

waterspouts **10:**754

Watson, James **1:**73

wavelengths

electromagnetic **2:**144; **3:***221*; **6:**404

light **2:**144, 145; **3:**218; **6:**404; **7:**553

wave–particle duality

light **6:**405; **7:**529, 553, 557

matter **9:**648, 649

waves (sea) **2:**143; **10:786–787**

and coastal erosion **2:**142; **4:***254*

tidal (tsunamis) **3:**173, 205; **4:**273; **10:744–745**, 781, 787

waxes **6:**413

weak nuclear force **4:**277; **8:**585

carrier particles for **8:**585

weapons

halogen gas **5:***336*

nuclear **4:***271*

weather **2:**130; **10:788–790**

and El Niño and La Niña **3:236–238**

fronts **2:**135; **6:**439; **7:**485; **9:**663; **10:**789

maps **5:**387; **6:**439

National Weather Service (NWS) **5:**351; **7:**486, **520–521**

oceans influencing the **7:**547

satellites **2:**137; **5:**351, 371; **7:***485*, 521, 547

See also climate; clouds; lightning and thunder; meteorology; rain, sleet, and snow; seasons; winds

Weather Bureau **7:**521

weather forecasts **1:**25; **7:**485, 486, 520–521, 547

and radar **3:**193; **7:**487, 521; **9:**659

monsoons **7:**507

weathering **5:**395; **8:**565; **9:**687

Weddell Sea **1:**50

weeks **2:**85

Wegener, Alfred **2:**156; **4:**318; **8:**582, 622

weight, and mass **5:**327; **6:**450

weightlessness **10:791**

welding **4:**293; **8:**617

wells **5:**331, 357

artesian **5:**331

Wells, H. G. **10:**752, *753*

westerlies **5:**386; **10:**788, 797

Western Australian Shield **1:**60

West Indies **2:**102

wetlands **2:**142; **10:792–793**

whirlpools, in the oceans **7:**549

whirlwinds **10:**754

white dwarfs **1:**67, 76; **7:**523, *536*, 537; **9:**718; **10:794**

White, Edward **1:**37; **4:**297, 298, *299*

Whiterock rock series **7:**558

white smokers **5:**359

Wien, Wilhelm **9:**646

williwaws **8:**576

WIMPs **10:**771

winds **1:**51; **10:**788, 790, **795–797**

causing ocean currents **7:***543*

and the Coriolis effect **1:**25; **10:**790, 795

and El Niño **3:**236–237, *238*

erosion by **3:**185; **4:**255

scales **10:**755, 796

trade **1:**22, 25, 49; **3:**236, 237, 238; **5:**387; **8:**576; **10:**761, 788, 797

See also hurricanes; jet streams; monsoons; tornadoes

Winkler, Clemens Alexander **8:**594

Wöhler, Friedrich **1:**30, 69

wormholes **1:**77; **10:**753

W particles **8:**585, 586

Wright, Wilbur and Orville **1:**18

Wyville, Charles **6:**442–443

Xenon **4:**295

X rays **3:**177, 221; **10:798**

and barium sulfate **6:**469

from space **1:***44*, 77; **4:**261

and mineralogy **7:**491

X-ray diffraction **1:**72; **10:**798

xylem **2:**93

Years

leap **4:***250*

solar **2:**84

yeast **2:**105, 123

Yellowstone National Park **2:**113; **4:**309; **5:**331

Yosemite National Park **4:**254

Yosemite valley **5:**367

Young, John **4:**297, 298

Young, Thomas **6:***405*–406; **7:**557

yttrium **8:**594

Yucatán peninsula, meteorite impact **3:**173; **4:***265*; **6:**476

Yukon River **9:***671*

Zaire River **1:**21

Zambezi River **1:**21

zeolites **3:**191; **5:**374

zinc **5:**379; **8:**571

zodiac **2:**155; **4:**250

Zond spacecraft **1:**36; **9:**675

Z particles **8:**585, 586

Zweig, George **8:**586, 613; **10:**727

Volume numbers appear in **boldface type** followed by colons. Page numbers in **boldface type** refer to main articles and their illustrations. Page numbers in *italic type* refer to additional illustrations.

550 EXP #11	Exploring Earth and Space Science		

05/06	**DATE DUE**